"Well, well, well," ~~she~~
said lightly. "Jim Trent, as I live
and breathe. What brings you
back to our one-horse town?"

He refused to be baited. "It was time," he said.
"How are you, Suzy?"

"Swell—just don't call me Suzy."

He gave her a crooked grin and stepped up beside
her, draping his hands over the guard-rail. "I
thought everybody did," he said reasonably.

"Everybody used to, way back when I was a kid."
She shoved her hair away from her face, feeling as
skittish as a colt. "You've been gone a long time,
Trent. I'm a teacher now, and teachers can't
answer to 'Suzy'. Teachers need dignity."

He threw back his head and laughed. "I used to
believe that myself, until I got to know a few
teachers up close and personal, as they say.
Teachers are human like the rest of us, Suzy-Q."

She couldn't stop her rueful laughter. "Don't let it
get around, okay? Just don't call me Suzy, or you
may be starting something you can't finish, Jim
Trent."

"Anything I start with you I'll be more than
capable of finishing—and that's a promise."

Ruth Jean Dale comes from a newspaper family. She herself was a reporter for years and her husband is the editor of a small Southern California daily. Even her youngest daughter works as a journalist.

Recent titles by the same author:

RUNAWAY HONEYMOON
BREAKFAST IN BED

WILD HORSES!

BY
RUTH JEAN DALE

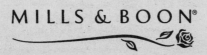

MILLS & BOON®

With gratitude to my Romance editors,
who went above and beyond to help make this
one work; and to Aunt Daisy and Aunt Patty,
just because.

First published in Great Britain 1997
Harlequin Mills & Boon Limited,
Eton House, 18-24 Paradise Road, Richmond, Surrey, TW9 1SR

© Betty Duran 1997

ISBN 0 263 80545 X

Set in Times Roman 10 on 12 pt.
02-9801-48830 C1

Printed and bound in Great Britain
by Mackays of Chatham PLC, Chatham

PROLOGUE

SUZANNAH GLENN closed her plastic-covered menu with a snap and faced her father across a scarred wooden tabletop at the Lobo Café in Addison, Wyoming. "But I don't *want* a steak," she announced. "I want a salad."

"Don't give me that." Rex Glenn harrumphed. "Nobody who lives in cow country eats rabbit food on purpose. Beef's our business."

"Beef's *your* business. Mine is educating the unformed little minds of Addison County." Suzannah glanced up at the patient waiter, a skinny kid of sixteen she'd known all his life. "I'll have the Lobo Deluxe Garden Fresh Salad, Mike, and a glass of iced tea, please."

"Comin' right up, Suzannah. How about you, Mr. Glenn?"

Rex regarded his daughter with exaggerated disbelief. Although old enough at sixty-nine to be her grandfather, instead of her father, he remained a handsome and imposing individual with hawklike features and upright bearing. His steel-gray hair, thick as a boy's, was his one vanity. He had it styled regularly at the Shear Magic Beauty Shoppe and Tonsorial Parlor.

"Bring me a steak sandwich," he instructed, "and I don't want to hear it mooing on the plate." He hesitated, giving his daughter a sly glance before adding, "I'll take a batch of those curly fries, too."

"Pop, you know you're not supposed to eat that greasy stuff," Suzannah moaned.

Rex ignored her outburst. "What you waitin' for, boy?" he demanded of the waiter. "Hop to it."

Mike straightened. "Yessir. And I'll bring your coffee right away." He hurried off without waiting for an affirmative from the rancher.

Even when Rex leaned back in his chair, he managed to look commanding. Suzannah was just about the only resident of Addison County who could—or would—stand up to the man. Not that he was a bully, she always said to comfort herself; he was simply used to having his own way.

He was in for a big disappointment this time, she thought with pleasure—not that she'd ever disagree with him simply for the sake of argument. Heavens, no!

Mike plunked down a tall plastic glass of tea and a chipped ceramic mug, into which he splashed coffee. Suzannah, stripping the paper wrapper from a straw and thinking about how transparent her father's machinations were, smiled.

"What you grinnin' about?" Rex demanded. "You don't even know why I invited you to eat with me."

"You call that an invitation? 'Meet me at the Lobo—I got somethin' to tell you' is hardly an invitation."

Rex dumped sugar into his coffee and stirred vigorously; he did everything vigorously. "Who are you all of a sudden? Emily Post?"

"Miss Manners calls the shots these days."

"Maybe for you baby boomers."

"I'm no baby boomer. I'm only twenty-six years old! Give me a break, okay?"

"Why? You never give me one. Hell, girl, you were supposed to be a joy and comfort to me in my old age, not a thorn in my side during my prime, which you are."

"Time to bring out the violins?" She sawed away with an imaginary bow while rolling her sherry-colored eyes toward the ceiling. "Cut to the chase, Pop. You want me to move back to the ranch during summer break."

Rex laughed without shame. "You got a problem with that?"

"Only that you've pulled this on me every summer since I started teaching and moved into town."

"And every summer you give in," he said with plain satisfaction. "So what's wrong with that?"

"I'll tell you what's wrong with that—I'm perfectly happy living with Miss Louise. Besides, this summer I'm handling the children's reading program for the library and doing a little tutoring on the side. It's more convenient living here in town."

Rex looked hurt. "So your convenience is more important than your old father's happiness, is it?" He shook his head sadly. "The fact that I just rattle around in that big old ranch house doesn't pack any weight with you, I suppose. No, didn't think so."

Suzannah groaned. "Don't you try to do this to me again. You're never there, anyway, so why you put up such a fuss every—"

"Watch it, you kids!"

At Mike's shouted warning, Suzannah looked up and Rex swiveled around. Mike was hopping about trying to catch his balance, a large tray with their lunch order waving over his head. His efforts to save the day were hampered by three young girls who squealed in distress while they tried to scurry out of his path.

Three young girls who'd been in Suzannah's fifth-grade class last year. She half rose, holding her breath, afraid Mike was going to step on one of them or turn the tray upside down on their heads.

Instead, the boy managed to swing the tray down in front of him where he could steady it with his other hand. When he realized he'd averted disaster, his voice rose.

"What d'you girls think you're doing, running through here like a pack of coyotes?" He glared into three repentant faces, zeroing in on one. "Brittany Daniels, I'm gonna tell your big brother on you."

"We're sorry, Mike." The smallest of the three girls looked at her friends for confirmation, which they provided with decisive nods. "We need to see Miss Glenn *right away*. It's important."

Suzannah waved the girls over. "No harm done, Mike," she cajoled. "I'll make sure they behave themselves."

"Yeah, right." Grumbling under his breath while darting indignant glances at the girls, Mike served the food.

Suzannah gave her three cowed visitors a sympathetic grin. "Have you girls had lunch?"

"Oh, yes," Brittany said, still breathless. Jessica and Ashley nodded.

"In that case, do you think it would it be all right with your mothers if you had an ice-cream cone?"

Nods and big smiles answered her. She looked hopefully at Mike. With a grunt of reluctant acquiescence, he marched away, still rigid with displeasure.

"Chocolate!" the girls called after him, but he gave no sign he heard.

"So, what's so important?" Suzannah asked curiously.

"Oh, Miss Glenn, wait'll you hear—"

Rex, who'd watched events unfold with impatience, cut in. "Don't stand there like a gaggle of geese just passin' by," he scolded the youngsters. "Pull up some chairs and set down like your mamas taught you to, nice and polite."

"Yes, Mr. Glenn," they chorused.

When everyone was situated and ice-cream cones served, Suzannah smiled encouragingly at the girls. "Now, what's this all about?"

Jessica bounced up and down in her chair, too excited to sit still. "We just heard that some wild horses—"

"Let me tell it!" Brittany shot her friend an incensed glance. "It was my brother told us."

Rex banged a heavy fist on the table. "Wild horses!"

Brittany nodded, unperturbed. "Matt said he heard about it out at the Box L. Said one of the hands was talking about wild horses on the other side of Green Valley. But guess what, Miss Glenn, guess what? The leader is a white stallion, Matt said! Oh, Miss Glenn, it sounds just like Pegasus, the flying horse we studied last year in mythology!"

What it sounded like to Suzannah was trouble with a capital T. Wild horses were rare around Addison County, and never welcome; they trampled fields and gardens and fences, ate grass intended for ranch stock and lured or stole away domestic horses.

But even more of a problem was her father's almost irrational hatred of wild horses, a hatred known near and far—to everybody except ten- or eleven-year-old girls enraptured with the romance of all horses but especially wild ones. And a white stallion to boot. This was the stuff dreams were made of.

Rex, apparently unwilling to glare at three little girls chattering like chipmunks, glared, instead, at Suzannah. Why Rex felt so strongly about wild horses no one seemed to know, not even Suzannah; he did, and that was pretty much that.

Up until now, his wild-horse phobia had been a rather minor bone of contention between father and daughter—minor because wild horses so rarely ventured into their domain. True, Suzannah automatically tended to take the opposite side to any chosen by her father, but in this case, she felt strongly about the issue for more important reasons.

Although she was a dyed-in-the-wool animal lover, her interest went far deeper because . . .

She hadn't thought of it in ages, but once, years ago, she'd actually *seen* a wild white stallion. Could this possibly be the same animal?

She'd been almost sixteen at the time, and doing something she shouldn't have been doing: trespassing on the Crazy Ace Ranch. Was it her fault the Crazy Ace had the best swimming hole in the country? Or that it shared a boundary with her father's Monarch Ranch, placing temptation squarely in her path?

None of the other ranchers would have been stingy about their swimming holes, but Ace Kilmer wasn't called "Crazy Ace" for nothing. Suzannah felt a tremor of guilt at thinking of him that way now, since he'd died so recently, but facts were facts.

The chattering girls and her wrathful father faded from her consciousness when Suzannah thought about that day. As memories came rushing back, she smiled....

Ace's only ranch hand at the time had been a boy a few years older than she, a boy named Jim Trent. She'd had a wild crush on Trent, which was what everyone called him. He was the best-looking thing she'd ever seen, not to mention magnificently confident and a magnet to every teenage girl in the county. But he'd also been something of a loner and no one seemed to know him really well, with the possible exception of his cousin, Rod, who was a few years younger.

He was also the only cowboy who seemed able to get along with the irascible Ace. Thus it was Trent who discovered her that uncharacteristically steamy day, swimming in the buff in Wild Horse Creek. When she'd started wading toward shore, he'd had the common—or not so common—decency to clear his throat just in the nick of time. Gasping, she'd hunched chin-deep in the water, casting about frantically for the Peeping Tom.

It took her a few moments to spot him, sitting his horse well back in dappled shadow and sunlight beneath the trees. And when she did, she realized he was laughing at her.

Before she could give him a piece of her mind, a new sound intruded, and she darted a glance over one shoulder. What she saw stemmed the flow of angry words she'd meant to hurl at Trent.

A magnificent white horse stepped from the trees just downstream. He stood for a moment sniffing the wind, his nostrils flaring. Framed as he was by a backdrop of deep green, the stallion looked like some wondrous mythical creature conjured up in a sweet wild dream.

Suzannah held her breath, sinking lower still, until the water came to just below her nose. The stallion hadn't seen her or he'd have been long gone. Nor had he seen Trent, who was well hidden, unless his horse gave him away.

Glancing toward the opposite bank without turning her head, she saw that Trent had dismounted to stand beside his horse, his hand on the animal's nose.

Downstream, the stallion approached the water's edge his silver hide glinting as he moved through shafts of sunlight. Several mares emerged from the trees behind him. He snorted and his great dark eyes flashed. Suzannah had never seen a more beautiful sight, and fully expected Trent must feel the same way.

But she was in for a shock, for when she looked back at Trent she saw that, far from being awestruck, he'd stealthily retrieved his lariat from the saddle. While she watched in growing alarm, he began to creep soundlessly downstream toward the wild horses.

Suzannah couldn't believe her eyes. How dared he contemplate capture of that fantastic animal! Not while she could prevent it, she decided.

With a bloodcurdling shriek, she shot out of the water, spraying torrents in all directions. Who she startled most—man or stallion—was hard to say, for both bolted upright as if jabbed by the same cattle prod.

In the next instant the stallion reared, neck arched and hooves pawing the air. The sight was breathtaking, even in retrospect. Then he'd turned tail and, pushing his harem before him, disappeared back the way he'd come.

Jim Trent also watched the horses go, disgust in every line of his lanky body. Turning toward the girl cowering in Wild Horse Creek, he'd—

"Miss Glenn, Miss Glenn!"

Suzannah shook off the memories with an effort. "What is it, Ashley?"

"Your daddy says—"

"Doggone it!" Rex looked determined, despite the youthful disapproval being showered upon him. "I said it and I mean it. If that wild herd knows what's good for it, it won't even *think* about coming into Addison County." His brown eyes narrowed dangerously. "Lots of perils for wild critters around here, from prairie-dog holes to stray bullets. Accidents happen all the time—"

"We've got federal authorities to protect wild animals," Suzannah cut in, the light of battle in her eyes.

Rex snorted. "Yep, but they can't keep track of every single critter, now can they."

"Miss Glenn, is something bad going to happen to the wild horses?" Jessica wailed.

Suzannah glared at her father. "Over my dead body," she vowed. She patted Jessica's hand, speaking to all three girls. "Don't worry. I'll make sure nobody messes with those horses—and that includes you, Pop."

Ashley glanced doubtfully from father to daughter. "I dunno, Miss Glenn...."

"Trust me," Suzannah said firmly. "I'll take care of this." Not liking the set expression on her father's face, she added, "Besides, Green Valley's a long way off. It's probably nothing more than a rumor."

Please let it be a rumor.

CHAPTER ONE

JIM TRENT CLOSED the corral gate and glanced at his cousin. "Solid," he said with satisfaction, banging a fist on a post, which didn't even quiver. "All of it's solid—house, barn, corrals."

Rod Lowell shoved his hat to the back of his head. "It sure is." He looked puzzled. "After you quit workin' here and went to rodeoin', that crazy old coot couldn't get anybody else to work for him for more than a few weeks at a time. I don't know how he kept things up so good."

"That was Ace's way—to take care of things," Trent said softly. "What he couldn't hire done he'd do himself, even if it took him a month. The only reason people called him crazy was because he didn't give a hoot in hell what they thought or said about him. Nobody seemed to understand that he had a generous heart—"

"And no next of kin," Rod inserted with a wry chuckle. "Were you surprised, him leavin' this place to you when he died?"

Good question. Trent leaned back against the corral and crossed his arms over his chest, considering. He'd worked for Ace off and on for almost five years; they'd become friends, the curmudgeonly rancher and the green kid. It'd been Ace's idea to send Trent off to test himself in the wide world outside Addison County.

So was he surprised that the old man remembered him ten years later?

"Not really." Trent smiled at his memories. "Although I can recall many a time when the old guy'd get mad at somebody hereabouts—usually Rex Glenn—and he'd rant and rave and swear he was going to leave this place to the BLM just to get even."

Rod joined in laughter at the expense of everybody's favorite target, the Bureau of Land Management. "Guess he figured you'd give the locals more trouble in the long run than the BLM ever could," he suggested.

Trent shrugged, amused. "Hey, I've reformed," he objected. "I'm just a good ol' boy, lookin' to get along."

He started toward the house, and Rod fell into step beside him. "I suppose everybody knows," Trent said.

Rod held open the back screen door. "About what? You givin' up rodeo?"

Trent shot his cousin a sharp glance. "That's family business. I mean about Ace leavin' me this place."

"I doubt it." Rod followed Trent onto the porch. "I only found out myself a coupla days ago. Pa warned me to keep my mouth shut until you decide whether you're gonna stay or sell."

That startled Trent, since there wasn't the slightest possibility he'd sell the Crazy Ace. Somehow he felt a deep responsibility, as if the ranch had been left to him almost like a trust. But he didn't tell his cousin that, simply shrugged. Revelation had never come easily to him. From time to time, he'd even been called secretive.

Usually by women.

"Everybody'll know my business soon enough," he predicted mildly. "No use depriving them of the fun of hearin' it on the grapevine first. So what else has been goin' on in this neck of the woods? Been a long time since I've been home."

"Ah, not much." Rod reached into the cooler situated in a corner of the porch and pulled out a beer. "Rex Glenn's braggin' about a coupla new mares he bought in Denver, Miss Louise gave the town a new library building, Stanley's Feed Store's added a repair shop for farm equipment."

Trent disposed of the twist-off cap from his beer bottle and took a swig. "Same old Addison," he said, but with a certain fondness he'd discovered only after he left.

Rod grinned. "Oh, and Matt Daniels says there's a herd of wild horses drifting this way."

Trent's interest immediately perked up several notches. "Now that's a surprise."

Rod nodded. "Damn straight. Funny thing is, the band's led by a light-colored stallion, maybe even white. Seems kinda unlikely, but that's what they're sayin'."

The hair on Trent's nape prickled. He'd seen a wild white stallion once, a long time ago. It had happened right here on the Crazy Ace, ten or eleven years back when he'd still been a wet-behind-the-ears twenty.

Man, what a waste of good horseflesh! He'd wanted to throw a loop on that stallion in the worst way—a loop and then a saddle. He could have ridden the animal then; hell, he could have ridden anything on four legs then. Could he now—and survive whole?

He scowled and rubbed absently at his right knee. What did doctors know, anyway?

Rod was regarding his cousin with a puzzled expression. "You got a real funny look on your face, Trent. Way back when, you were always wantin' to chase off after wild horses. You still got that bug?"

"Hell, yes!" Trent took a long swallow of cold beer. "Ace used to tell me what it was like back in the old days. He chased a few wild horses himself in his younger years. 'Son,' he used to say, 'you tangle with a herd of wild hosses and it'll sure separate the men from the boys in a hurry.'"

"That's the truth," Rod agreed. "I always wanted to give it a try."

"Me, too," Trent said. "I almost got my chance...."

The girl had messed everything up—not "the girl"; he knew her name. Suzannah Glenn, daughter of the toughest old sonuvabitch in Wyoming. When Trent had started toward the white stallion that day, she'd come up out of that water like she'd been shot from a canyon, screaming like a banshee.

Thinking about it, he grinned, although he hadn't grinned at the time. In fact he'd been furious. Way he figured it, Suzannah Glenn owed him one—no, two, because Ace had been hard on trespassers and Trent had got all softheaded and let her go with just a stern warning.

She'd been a cute little thing in those days: young—no more than fifteen or sixteen—and spunky. It took spunk to lead that pigheaded pa of hers around on a string like she did.

When Trent had caught her skinny-dipping in Wild Horse Creek, he'd glimpsed more temptation than she'd realized. He'd told himself she was too young, which she was, and he'd let her go, albeit reluctantly.

But that was then and this was now. She'd be in her midtwenties, all grown up.... He looked out over the high plains of Wyoming, toward the rough country to the northeast, mulling it over in his mind.

So the wild herd was back, was it? Maybe this time, things would be different. Maybe this time, he'd take the horse—and the girl, too.

SUZANNAH SAT on a low stool in a corner of the children's room in the Addison Library looking out at the eager and attentive faces of eleven elementary-school-age youngsters. She closed the book she'd been reading aloud and smiled encouragingly. "And then what happened?" she prompted.

"They lived happily ever after!" the children chorused, all except ten-year-old Joshua who pretended to stick his finger down his throat while making rude gagging noises.

Suzannah ignored him. "So what shall we read next week?" she asked, putting the book of fairy tales aside.

"Stephen King!" Joshua threw himself on the floor and flopped around, pretending to strangle himself while emitting a variety of pants and grunts and gasps.

"Joshua Hickman, what do you know about Stephen King?" Suzannah demanded.

The freckle-faced boy sat up suddenly with a sunny smile. "Nothing," he admitted, "except my brother says there's lots of blood and guts." He turned toward Brittany Daniels with his fingers curved like talons and a snarl on his lips.

She rewarded him with a little shriek of revulsion. "You quit that, Joshua!" she cried. "Miss Glenn, me and Ash—"

"Ash and I, Brittany."

"That's right, and Jessica, too—we all want to read books about horses."

"Horses?" Joshua's interest perked up at once.

"Wild horses," Brittany amended pompously, "and mystical horses."

"Not mystical, honey," Suzannah corrected. "I think you mean mythical—like in the myths we read in class last year."

Brittany gave a queenly nod. "That's what I said, sure. Like Pegasus."

"Peg who?" Joshua demanded.

"You'll find out next year in fifth grade," Ashley said condescendingly.

"You know," Suzannah said slowly, "when I was a little girl, my grandfather told me wonderful stories about the White Stallion of the Plains. Perhaps in a way, those stories are American versions of the Pegasus myth."

She could still hear Grandpa's voice, although he'd been gone for many years now: "Folks were talkin' about that white stallion even back in my Grandpa Harlan's day—that's your great-great-grandpa, Suzygal. He was born in Oregon Territory and come to Wyoming as a fur trapper when he was just a younker. Don't recall him or anybody else actually sayin' they saw the animal, but they all claimed to know somebody who had."

She shivered. The magnificent wild stallion she and Jim Trent had seen on the banks of Wild Horse Creek that day seemed a perfect reincarnation of the legendary White Mustang. Since that initial—and only—sighting, she'd found herself thinking of him as Pegasus.

All the children were talking at once. Suzannah held up her hands and called for order. "I think that's a wonderful idea, Ashley. Is it all right with everyone else?"

Nods of agreement met this proposal, even from Joshua.

"Yeah, horses," he said. "All right!"

"Then next week, we'll all read books about horses and talk about what we've read here again on Saturday."

Suzannah watched her little group disperse, a smile on her lips. But when they'd all gone, the smile slipped.

Brittany had announced the return of the wild horses two days ago, and Suzannah had heard nothing since. Maybe when she stopped by Stanley's Feed Store to drop off the list of supplies her father needed, she could find out the latest gossip.

"Sorry, Suzannah," Paul Stanley said, halting with a bag of grain over one shoulder. "Haven't heard a word about that wild bunch. I'm startin' to think it was just another crazy rumor."

"You're probably right," she agreed hopefully. The way her father was stomping and snorting around the Monarch, no wild horse in its right mind would get within a hundred miles of him.

Which was exactly what she told Paul's sister, Jenny, later when the two teachers met for lunch at the Lobo.

"It's probably only a rumor, anyway," Jenny said. "Honestly, the whole thing sounds like a fairy tale to me."

Suzannah laughed, her friend's pessimism a familiar response. "What's wrong with fairy tales?" she teased. "Where's your romantic spirit?"

"I lost it years ago," Jenny grumbled, but she smiled when she said it. "There's just not that many wild horses left anymore, and those that are still out there simply aren't the stuff of legend."

"I could argue that point," Suzannah said, "but I won't. I'm just going to pray that if there is a band of wild horses, they don't get anywhere near my father."

Jenny uttered a heartfelt "amen!"

"On the other hand, this has presented a wonderful opportunity to get the kids in my Saturday-morning reading circle interested in something other than cartoons and comic books."

Jenny reached for a french fry. "You've always been good at finding the silver lining," she said. "Not to change the subject or anything, but do you have a date for the dance tonight?"

"Afraid not." Suzannah picked up a fry and tore it in half. "Guess I'll just ride in with my father— Oops!" She caught herself too late.

"Suzannah Glenn! You've moved back out to the Monarch? Your father's done it to you again!" Laughing, Jenny leaned her cheek on her hand.

"So what else is new?" Suzannah smiled ruefully. Although her father would deny it, it seemed to her that no matter how good a fight she put up, he always won in the end. "Are you going to the dance with Rod?"

Jenny frowned. "Yes, although what good it'll do me..."

Suzannah didn't know what to say. She, more than anyone else, understood how hard it had been for Jenny to come back to Addison from Los Angeles two years ago, after her divorce. Once burned and twice shy, she'd resisted Rod's attentions for months, but he'd eventually worn her down.

They'd been seeing each other for nearly a year now, but Rod had shown no interest whatsoever in taking the next logical step in the relationship.

"So how about you?" Jenny inquired brightly. "Isn't it about time you started looking for Mr. Right?"

"In a town the size of Addison, I think I'd know if he was here."

"This is no joking matter." Jenny sipped coffee, her hazel eyes thoughtful. "Sometimes I think if your father wasn't so determined to see you married and settled down, you would be already. Every time you two have a run-in on the subject, I see your standards rise just a little bit higher. At this point, I don't think even Mel Gibson could please you."

"That," Suzannah said forcefully, "is ridiculous. Mel Gibson could please me plenty."

"That's what you say, but I wonder. Maybe what you need is a challenge." Jenny cocked her head and grinned impishly. "Jim Trent's back."

"What!" Suzannah's jaw dropped. "You're kidding, right?"

"I am not. I saw him at the post office earlier today. Didn't have a chance to grill him—" she paused long enough for a suggestive wink "—so I don't know how long he'll be staying. But I'm here to tell you he is one fine-lookin' cowboy.'' Jenny whistled softly beneath her breath and rolled her eyes.

Jim Trent was back. Strange timing, almost disturbing really, considering Suzannah had been thinking about him so much lately. Although they'd never discussed what had happened that day on Wild Horse Creek—and Trent had left shortly after that to go on the rodeo circuit—she'd still felt a special connection between them each time they'd run into each other over the years. And on a few occasions, she'd thought she'd seen a kind of speculative look in his eyes.

Regardless of that, the mere thought of his showing up in Addison at this particular time, when the wild white stallion might be on the loose, flustered her considerably.

So she changed the subject. ''Are you still thinking of going on a shopping trip to Cheyenne, Jen? If you are, I think I'd like to go along....''

Later, picking up the supplies for the ranch, Suzannah tried to analyze her awkward reaction to hearing Trent's name said out loud. It had been especially silly because she was the only one who even knew he'd been there that day.

For months afterward, she'd rattled on to anyone who'd listen about seeing the wild white stallion. Trent, as far as she knew, had never told a soul.

At first that had annoyed her—she'd somehow expected he'd jump to her defense when people suggested she needed glasses or a little less imagination. But then she was glad, because she didn't want anyone to know she'd been trespassing on the Crazy Ace, or the exact location where she'd seen the wild herd.

Trent had probably forgotten all about the entire incident, although *she* never would, not if she lived to be a hundred.

On her way back to the ranch, habit asserted itself and she pulled into the horseshoe-shaped driveway leading up to the big old Victorian house on the outskirts of town. This was where she lived during the school year, with her godmother, Miss Louise Addison.

Miss Louise, the seventy-two-year-old maiden lady whose family had given the town its name, was always ready to offer support and encouragement. When Suzannah had graduated from the University of Wyoming and returned to a teaching job in Addison, it had seemed the most natural thing in the world to accept the invitation to live here. This house had been a second home to her, anyway, and she expected it always would be.

Over cookies and tea served in the dark old-fashioned parlor by Winnie, the housekeeper and cook, Suzannah felt herself relaxing. Miss Louise might intimidate others, but never her goddaughter. "So did you hear about the wild horses?" she asked when conversation lagged.

"I certainly did, and I'm astonished." Miss Louise didn't look astonished; she looked incensed. "It's been years since there's been a wild horse anywhere near this part of Wyoming. Although I must say, back in the old days they were a dime a dozen." She shrugged. "But you don't want to hear about all that."

"Of course I do. I love your stories about the old days," Suzannah objected. "I repeat most of them to my students." She smiled. "I never thought to ask permission. You don't mind, do you?"

"Mind? I'm delighted anyone still cares about the memories of an old maid like myself."

And indeed, Miss Louise did look pleased.

For the life of her, Suzannah couldn't understand why some man hadn't snapped Miss Louise up decades ago. Not only had she been a great beauty, as evidenced by the luminous portrait above the mantel, she'd been a cattle baron's daughter and had inherited a sizable fortune. Which she'd wisely invested, doubling and trebling it over and over again.

Now her hair was as silvery white as the coat of the wild stallion, but her figure was still slender and girlish and her mind as agile as it had ever been. What was the matter with men?

Suzannah reached for another cookie and Miss Louise snatched the plate away. "Three cookies are quite sufficient," she said, frowning the frown that made brave men cower. "So tell me, who's taking you to the dance tonight?"

"Guess." Suzannah eyed the cookie plate, finally deciding discretion really was the better part of valor.

"Your father, I would suppose."

"And you'd be right." Suzannah sipped her tea, handling the fragile china cup gently. "I wouldn't even go if I hadn't promised to help out."

"Suzannah, dear, what is lacking in young men nowadays?"

Suzannah grinned; that was exactly what she'd been thinking about the young men back in Miss Louise's day. "There's nothing wrong with them," she said lightly. "They're swell. They're just not . . . exciting."

"Really? May I gently point out to you that you're not getting any younger?"

Suzannah took this comment with good grace; she was used to such remarks. "Why be gentle? Just come right out with it. Pop does."

"For once he's right." Miss Louise sighed. "Dear, if you're not careful you'll end up like me—a shriveled-up old prune."

Suzannah burst out laughing. Miss Louise was a beautiful and elegant woman of mature years, the few lines on her face only adding character. At a mere five foot one, she possessed a regal bearing and incomparable charm—not to mention a will of iron.

"I'd be proud to end up like you," Suzannah declared with heartfelt sincerity. She placed her cup and saucer on the highly polished table. "And just for the record, nothing would make me happier than to fall in love and get married. But I won't settle for anything less than...than a grand passion!" She threw her arms wide in an expansive gesture. "You know how I am, Miss Louise. It's all or nothing."

Miss Louise smiled indulgently. "Looking at you sitting there pretty as a picture with your eyes all a-sparkle just makes me wish your father would stop pushing you long enough to let nature take its course."

"My father!" Suzannah slumped back on the brocaded settee. "What about present company, if I may be so bold?"

Miss Louise looked flustered. "Come now, I don't harp on the subject nearly as much as he does," she said defensively. "If you'd just let yourself fall in love..."

"Let myself?" Suzannah shook her head in disbelief. "That's easy for you to say."

"No, dear, it isn't." Miss Louise lifted her chin to a haughty angle. "I was in love once myself so I know whereof I speak."

"Really? I didn't know that."

"And you wouldn't know it now if you hadn't caught me in a pensive mood," Miss Louise said. "Let's change the subject, shall we? How are you and Rex getting on now that he's bullied you into returning to the ranch for the summer?"

HER PROBLEM, Suzannah thought later as she drove out to the Monarch, was that despite her reputation as a sensible and levelheaded schoolteacher, she had a romantic streak a mile wide. Quite simply, she longed to be swept off her feet.

She wanted romance, passion, fireworks—love, pure and true. What she *didn't* want was to go to that dance. If she hadn't promised to sell refreshments for the Town Beautification Committee, she'd beg off.

But go she must, which was why she found herself sitting beside her father in one of the ranch pickups that evening, rolling into town for the second time that day. She hadn't had a minute to talk to Rex since she'd returned with the supplies, so at the first opportunity—which came when he finally paused for breath in the midst of a rambling recitation about problems on the north range—she brought up the subject uppermost in her mind.

"Heard any more about the wild horses, Pop?"

"Huh?" Rex shot her a startled glance. "Not a word. Have you?"

"No. I asked at the feed store, but Paul didn't have any news. Thought maybe you'd know something."

"Well, I don't," he said curtly, "but when I do, you'll hear me all the way to Cheyenne."

She laughed, because his reaction was no more than she'd expected. As long as the wild herd remained nothing but a rumor, she could afford to be generous. They drove in silence for a few miles, and then she said, "Maybe tomorrow I'll ride out and take a look around, see if I can find any sign of them."

"Tomorrow never comes!" Rex snapped. He gentled his temper and his tone. "Look, I don't want you out messin' around with wild stock. You could get yourself hurt. Besides, I got me a better idea. How about us goin' to Cheyenne and pick you out a new car? Something nice and sporty—"

"My car's fine," she interrupted. "It's only three years old and has hardly any mileage."

"It's a wreck and I'm embarrassed to have you seen in it."

"*You're* embarrassed? You've got some nerve. I'll have you know..."

The merits of a new car were a nice safe topic to debate, so they did, all the way to the high-school parking lot. Rex wheeled the pickup into a space and they both climbed out, still arguing.

The debate ended, however, the minute they walked into the gymnasium where the dance was being held, for they were immediately surrounded: he by his cronies in the older set, she by her friends in the younger.

A few minutes later, Jenny and Rod nudged their way through to Suzannah's side. She knew, of course, that Rod was Jim Trent's cousin, younger by a couple of years. He looked so much like Trent that seeing him gave her a start.

"Glad you made it, Suzannah. We just got here ourselves." Rod tightened his arm around Jenny and grinned. "This is one hardhearted woman—made me wait while she changed clothes three times."

"Wasn't it worth it?" Jenny's glance was teasing and Rod responded with a quick light kiss on her lips.

Suzannah stifled a sigh. She was all in favor of romance, but wedding bells had already pretty much played hell with her social life. It made her lonely just thinking about Jenny and Rod getting serious.

Even as she laughed and joked, she tried to reassure herself that she wasn't going to end up the only old maid in her group—although it was beginning to look like a distinct possibility. Feeling like a fifth wheel, she grabbed her first chance to retire to the small gymnasium kitchen where a half-dozen women, all older than she, were setting up the big coffeepots and slicing homemade pies.

Suzannah was the only unmarried woman in the room. This knowledge did nothing to lift her spirits.

The dance quickly settled down into the same pattern as all the other community dances held in Addison. Rex and his cronies loitered outside a back door, smoking and gabbing. The older women—and Suzannah—worked ceaselessly to sell refreshments, clean up messes and make sure everyone else had a good time.

The young unmarried women lingered around the goody table and eyed the young men, dancing when they were invited. At one end of the gymnasium, a local country-and-western band played tirelessly; at the other end, Miss Louise held court, as befitted the town matriarch.

Carrying her godmother a cup of punch, Suzannah was surprised to hear the topic of conversation.

"... and the possibility of that herd being led by a wild white stallion is hardly the big news you all seem to think it is," Miss Louise was saying. "They've been telling stories throughout the West about the White Stallion of the Plains for a good 150 years." She added slyly, "Which is even longer than I've been around."

The crowd of ten or eleven laughed politely. It always paid to laugh at Miss Louise's little jokes, but mostly, Suzannah knew, they laughed because they liked and respected her.

"It's just a legend—there's not a word of truth in it," Miss Louise went on, accepting with a quick smile the cup of punch Suzannah offered. "I don't think anybody believes such an animal exists, except maybe romantic young girls." She winked at Suzannah.

This time the laughter was more than polite. There wasn't a person in the room who didn't know about Suzannah's contention that she'd seen a wild white stallion all those years ago.

Suzannah laughed along with everyone else. "I know what I know," she said serenely, "and I know what I saw. There *was* a white mustang and maybe he's returned—although I devoutly hope not, considering what my father is fully prepared to do to him." She shivered.

"Personally," Rod said, "I always thought Suzannah was dreaming. She was just a kid when she saw whatever she saw. I tend to think it was a pinto or a gray or maybe even a dun—some old crowbait, most likely, or even a stray from one of the ranches. Wild horses—" he shook his head "—hell, they just aren't what they're cracked up to be."

"You're wrong, Rod." Intensely aware of public attention, Suzannah wanted to back down but wouldn't when she was in the right. "He was snow white and as beautiful as the myths and legends say."

"And where did you say you saw this paragon of virtue?"

She laughed and shook her head. "Nice try, cowboy, but that's my secret."

"Well, there you have it." Rod glanced at Jenny for backup but she appeared to be trying hard to maintain neutrality and merely shrugged. "It's Suzannah's word against common sense," Rod argued. "Whoever saw that white stallion except her? Nobody, that's who."

Into the acquiescent silence, a deep familiar voice spoke from the back of the crowd. "Wrong, cousin. *I* did."

CHAPTER TWO

CATCHING HER BREATH, Suzannah turned as if drawn by a magnet. A murmur of surprise rose around her, giving voice to her own feelings. The crowd parted, pivoting as one to stare at the man standing alone at the back.

Jim Trent, Addison's favorite son, had come home. Everyone clustered around him except Miss Louise and Suzannah, who had the briefest glimpse of the tall cowboy before his admirers hid him from view.

That one glance was enough. She stifled a groan; he looked better than ever, which didn't seem possible for someone who'd started where he had.

Trent had always been a classic man of the West. Tall and lean with an easygoing manner that failed to mask the steel beneath, he was a man of action. Handsome didn't begin to describe what he was, although it provided a place to begin. Dark hair, blue eyes, skin browned by the sun, a face composed of high cheekbones and a strong jaw—his good looks had landed him in a couple of Western clothing advertisements early in his rodeo career.

Suzannah had burned with youthful jealousy when she'd realized that millions of women were looking at those same images and lusting after him—Jim Trent, who belonged to Addison and to her, at least in her fantasies.

By then, he'd already won his first rodeo titles and was quietly cocky and utterly sure of himself. She, on the other hand, was getting ready to graduate from high school—a nobody in the overall scheme of things. She'd had no reason to feel these pangs of possessiveness—there had never been so much as a hint of a personal relationship between them. It was just that they'd shared something special on Wild Horse Creek—even though he'd never once referred to it afterward.

All that came back in a rush. Then the boisterous crowd shifted and she found herself looking straight into Trent's eyes. He grinned and gave the barest nod in greeting, knocking her for another loop. She'd forgotten how powerful his personal magnetism was, and the reminder was potent.

Or maybe she'd been too much of a kid to really understand before.

Beside her, Miss Louise lifted one hand in a regal wave. This time Trent's acknowledgment was for the older woman, and he began working his way in their direction.

Despite his celebrity status, he wasn't dressed in cowboy chic. His jeans were well-worn and well-fitting, his shirt a subdued blue without spangles or gewgaws to detract from the muscular strength beneath. Even so, he looked like what he was: a hometown boy who'd made good. It was more in his manner than any trappings of success.

But now that he'd been granted an audience with Miss Louise, Suzannah had no intention of hanging around in the background waiting for crumbs of attention. Turning, she sidled toward the door leading outside.

She didn't quite understand why, knowing he was in town, she'd been so unprepared to see him. It was probably nothing more than the embarrassment of remembering how he'd caught her skinny-dipping in forbidden waters, she decided. Sure, that was it. Once he went back to his real life, she'd forget all about him for another decade or so.

He was simply here on one of his infrequent visits to the aunt and uncle who'd raised him—Rod's parents. He'd leave soon; he always did.

Brushing past a few idlers near the front door to the school, Suzannah walked outside and gulped a lungful of fresh night air. The rush of oxygen steadied her. Leaning against the metal guardrail, she looked up at a fathomless sky full of stars and gave herself a good talking-to.

She was doing just fine until a quiet voice behind her sent shivers down her spine.

"Evenin', Suzy. Run into any wild horses lately?"

She laughed. It was somehow a relief to have him bring it out in the open after all these years. With one deep final breath, she turned to face him. Hands gripping the rail behind her, she met Trent's amused gaze.

"Well, well, well," she said lightly. "Jim Trent, as I live and breathe. What brings you back to our one-horse town?"

He refused to be baited. "It was time," he said. "How are you, Suzy?"

"Swell—just don't call me Suzy."

He gave her a crooked grin and stepped up beside her, draping his hands over the guardrail. "I thought everybody did," he said reasonably.

"Everybody used to, way back when I was a kid." She shoved her hair away from her face, feeling skittish as a colt. "You've been gone a long time, Trent. I'm a teacher, now, and teachers can't answer to 'Suzy.' Teachers need dignity."

He threw back his head and laughed. "I used to believe that myself, until I got to know a few teachers up close and personal, as they say. Teachers are human just like the rest of us, Suzy-Q."

She couldn't stop her rueful laughter. "Don't let it get around, okay? The point is, I'm all grown up and I don't answer to silly nicknames anymore. It took a while, but I finally got that through to just about everyone except my father. So don't call me Suzy, or you may be starting something you can't finish, Jim Trent."

Her mock ferocity evaporated before his narrow-eyed regard.

"Anything I start with you I'll be more than capable of finishing—and that's a promise." A sudden and unexpected grin broke the tension. "But I'll be the first to admit you're all grown up." He gave her a once-over that made her want to squirm. "Your hair's different."

"I let it grow," she said lamely, stating the obvious.

"And it's all curly. It used to be short and straight. Looked real cute with water dripping off it."

"I got a perm," she said, exasperated. She couldn't believe he remembered how she used to wear her hair. She could hardly believe he remembered she was alive. "Everything else about me is natural, I swear," she added.

"I know."

What was that supposed to mean? Had he seen more of the "natural" her than she'd realized that day on Wild Horse Creek? Suzannah's cheeks grew warm with embarrassment and she shifted uncomfortably.

"But that's not what I wanted to talk to you about," he added.

She felt a stab of disappointment, which she quickly pushed aside. "That's a relief."

"Rod tells me a band of wild horses may be heading this way, perhaps led by a white stallion. Hearing that sure took me back."

The longing in his voice surprised her into meeting his pensive gaze. "Me, too," she admitted. "By the way, you were smart to keep your mouth shut about what we saw that day. I spent the next couple of years defending myself against all the people who thought I'd been hallucinating."

"Then how come you never called me as a character witness?"

She shrugged. "I don't know. I guess I figured that if you wanted to come forward, you would. Then you left and went on the rodeo circuit and that was that. It surprised me—surprised a lot of us—the way you took off."

"I suppose it looked a little sudden, but it wasn't. Ace fired me."

"What? But you'd been with him for years. Why'd he do a thing like that?" She frowned. "Unless he really was crazy."

"Crazy like a fox." Trent's low laughter was affectionate. "He thought I should see something of the world before I settled down to ranching. He'd been talkin' up rodeo to me for a couple of years and I was interested, but I hated to leave him, the old goat. So he fired me. If he hadn't, I'm not sure I'd ever have gone."

"Well, I'll be... So that's what happened." Suzannah had heard the warmth in Trent's voice. He'd really loved Ace Kilmer. "I suppose you know he died about five months ago?"

"Yeah, I know." Trent's lopsided grin made her long to comfort him somehow. "I wanted to come back for the funeral, but I was in the—" He clipped off whatever he'd been about to say, then added, "He left the Crazy Ace to me."

Suzannah gaped at him, realized her jaw had dropped and snapped her mouth shut. "You're kidding! You mean you're back to stay?"

"Here he is, gang! Trent!"

A crowd of young women and a few men surged through the open doorway and descended on Trent. He edged away, leaving her grateful to be ignored in the general rush to surround him.

She could hardly believe the way these women fawned all over him. It was positively outrageous, especially considering that most of them had known him forever. He wasn't some movie or rock star; he was a local boy. They'd grown up with him, for goodness' sake.

Watching the disgraceful display, a new thought struck her; if women who knew him reacted this way, what must it be like out there in the big wide world? He was probably besieged from all sides, offered his pick of sophisticated beauties.

No wonder he'd left Addison and a small-town existence with hardly a backward glance. Now that he'd inherited the Crazy Ace, would he be satisfied very long as a big frog in a small pond? It didn't seem any too likely to Suzannah, not with the glamorous life of a rodeo star calling him.

Backing farther into the shadows, she watched him handle the cluster of fans with grace and charm. Over the heads of his admirers, Trent's gaze met hers. He raised his brows in acknowledgment, as if they were privy to each other's thoughts.

It rocked her, this silent communion. She didn't know him well enough that he should be able to read her mind, or she his. Turning sharply, she bumped into Rod. Jenny stood beside him, smiling and shaking her head as if she found the fuss as hard to believe as Suzannah did.

"Will you look at that?" Rod demanded, his tone heavy with disdain. "You'd think those women never saw a cowboy before."

Jenny gave him an oblique glance filled with amusement he didn't seem to notice. "That's what you'd think, all right. Is that a touch of jealousy I detect?"

Rod reared back, laying on the astonishment. "Not hardly! Now, if he'd been out here alone with my girl, I might have felt a touch of—"

"Fat chance—and what makes you think I'm your girl?" But Jenny was laughing.

Suzannah laughed, too. Things seemed to be developing nicely between Jenny and Rod. If man was not meant to live by bread alone, then neither was woman. Jenny's divorce had been brutal, and she deserved to be half of a happy pair.

Everybody did. Suzannah glanced quickly at Trent, then away just as fast.

Rod was still teasing Jenny. "I know darn good and well that you're one woman who won't fall for all that glamour." He glowered anew at the clustering females. He seemed to realize rather belatedly that they weren't alone and added hastily, "You and Suzannah, of course. She's got too much sense to fall for all that."

Jenny gave him a pained look. "Stop while you're ahead," she suggested. "Assuming you are."

Suzannah arched her brows. "He is, he is. You don't have to worry about me losing my head over just another pretty face." But she felt guilty about her own joke; Trent was definitely not just another pretty face.

Rod didn't seem to notice. "See?" He shot Jenny a glance of vindication. "But look at them others, buzzin' about Trent like bees around a hive. Pitiful."

Rod's foolishness had lightened Suzannah's spirits considerably. Thinking it was probably time for her to go inside and see if the dance had been permanently derailed, she heard a shout, which pulled her up short.

"Lemme through, lemme through!"

An overwrought man pushed his way up the steps toward the schoolhouse door. Wading through the crowd, Martin Young saw Trent and stopped short. "Jim Trent, you old son of a gun! When'd you hit town?"

Trent clasped the shorter man's hand and pumped it heartily. "Martin. Rolled in just a day or two ago. What's the trouble?"

"It's that damned wild bunch." Martin lifted his Stetson from his head and shoved a hand through his thin hair. He caught sight of Suzannah and snorted. "I got to admit, I thought Suzannah was crazy, talkin' about that white mustang the way she used to do. But no more—no, nosiree-bob, no more."

Suzannah's heart stood still. "Martin, you saw the wild bunch?"

"Damn straight I did. May have even seen that stallion. Just such a beast as you described stole one of my best mares."

"A white stallion?" Suzannah's mouth felt dry and a vague feeling of déjà vu swept over her. Somehow it seemed inevitable that Trent and the wild horses had come back at the same time.

Martin nodded vigorously. "If he wasn't pure white, I'll pay for lyin'!"

Jenny looked from the rancher to her friend, frowning. "I don't know," she said. "It's nighttime, so there's always the possibility of a mistake. Seems unlikely it'd be the same animal after all these years. Wouldn't he be pretty old?"

Suzannah drew a quick light breath and glanced at Trent. He stood perfectly still, his expression thoughtful.

Martin was speaking. "If that thief wasn't white, he was the next thing to it, Jenny. Big devil danged sure *looked* like Suzannah's phantom, and I'd swear to it in a court of law."

"He's not *my* phantom," Suzannah objected. "I said I saw a wild horse like that once, that's all." She couldn't resist adding, "Of course, nobody believed me at the time."

"So what you gonna do about your mare, Martin?" someone called from the crowd.

"Why, I'm—"

He was interrupted by an explosion of more men and boys through the schoolhouse door, Rod Lowell in the lead. Suzannah hadn't even realized he'd gone inside. While the men closed in on Martin and Trent, the women backed out of the circle, relegated to the status of curious onlookers, instead of participants.

Suzannah glanced around for her father and didn't see him. Just about everybody else was here, though, and excited questions flew back and forth.

This was serious business to the men of Addison. Most of them were ranchers and cowboys, and anything that messed with a man's livestock messed with his livelihood.

Anything that took away a man's horse was an offense to be dealt with—with expediency.

And Trent was right in the middle of it, as if he truly belonged there. Had he really come back to stay? If he had, he'd be a force to be reckoned with.

Rex Glenn burst through the schoolhouse door, his craggy face determined-looking. Zeroing in on Trent, he elbowed his way through the circle of friends and neighbors until he faced the younger man.

Their glances locked, two strong men measuring each other. The excited buzz of conversation trailed away, and all attention centered on the rancher and the rodeo champion.

Suzannah held her breath, not knowing quite what to expect. She had little idea how her father felt about Trent, beyond the fact that the younger man had turned down a job at the Monarch years ago.

Looking at the two of them now, she was struck for the first time by how alike they were. Both were tall hard men who rode their own trails and fought their own battles. If they ever clashed . . . She shivered.

If they ever clashed, it wouldn't happen now. A huge grin split Rex's face. "Jim Trent, you old hoss thief," he exclaimed. "Good to have you back, son!"

He grabbed Trent's hand and shook it hard, all the while pounding away on the younger man's shoulder.

A sigh of relief ran through the circle of onlookers, relief Suzannah shared.

Rex released Trent with a final slap on the shoulder and turned to Martin, all business. "So what's goin' on here? Rod said something about you losin' a mare to a wild stud—that right?"

Martin nodded vigorously. "Rex, it's that white stallion of Suzannah's, sure as the world," he announced.

"Now just a dad-gummed minute." Rex glanced at his daughter as if hoping she hadn't heard, which of course she had. "That hoss is nothin' but trouble on the hoof, and she's not gonna have a thing to do with him. It's not her hoss, anyway—never has been and never will be."

She shrugged. "I told them that," she said, denying any part in these goings-on.

Rex seemed satisfied. "Good, 'cause I won't have you messin' with a wild stallion—if one's really out there. Martin, it's been years since Suzannah quit runnin' around the countryside talkin' about that hoss. Now the first broomtail anybody sees, they automatically assume it's that one."

Martin's confidence seemed shaken; he frowned. "I dunno, it sure looked like a white hoss to me and I don't figure there're too many of 'em out there." He perked up. "But whatever it was, it made off with that little bay mare of mine and I want her back!"

A general murmur of sympathy greeted this pronouncement. "We're with you, Martin," one of the young men yelled.

"Now wait a minute, everybody." Suzannah advanced to stand by her father's side. "Let's talk about this calm—"

"Stay out of this, honey." Rex dismissed her with a pat on the arm. "It's no business for a woman. Us men'll take care of—"

"Rex Glenn, for shame!" Miss Louise had no trouble making herself heard. Small and sprightly, she glared at the big rancher. "Who d'you think you're bluffing? There are women in this town who can outride and maybe even outrope you any day of the week."

"Now, Louise," Rex said in a pained voice, "back off. This *is* men's business."

Suzannah tugged at his shirtsleeve. "It's everybody's business, Pop. If wild horses have wandered off their usual range, we need to get them back where they belong. What we *don't* need is anybody throwing around threats."

"Now, Suzy—"

"Don't 'now, Suzy' me." She turned on Martin Young. "What do you plan to do, Martin?"

"Offer a reward," the man announced. "How's five hundred dollars sound?"

Rod let out a long low whistle. "Like music to our ears, huh, boys?"

They confirmed his opinion noisily.

Suzannah looked around the circle of men, not liking their avid expressions. She could almost see the lust for the hunt in every eye—with one exception. Jim Trent looked ... thoughtful.

She squared her shoulders and faced Martin. "That's five hundred dollars for the return of the mare, right?"

"Sure. What else?"

She all but sagged with relief. Turning away, her gaze met Trent's and she realized he'd read her mind again. She'd feared the reward might also extend to the capture or killing of the wild stallion. Apparently emotions weren't yet running quite that high, but what would happen if the stallion didn't mend his thieving ways?

Martin shook a fist in the air. "So whaddaya say, boys? You with me? Truck your horses out to my place and we'll leave at first light. Marty, how about you and your friends?"

"We're with you, Pa!" Marty shouted.

"I'll be there," Rex announced, "along with as many riders as the Monarch can spare."

"Much obliged," Martin grunted. "Knew I could count on you, Rex. How about you, Trent?"

"Well, I'll tell you how it is..."

Trent's lazy drawl brought all other conversation to a halt. It was as if he'd been lying back, figuring out his position, and now would tell the rest of them how things were going to be.

Suzannah could almost see her father's ears prick up while he waited for Trent to go on.

"Yeah?" Martin urged.

"I want that stallion," Trent said.

Suzannah felt as if he'd punched her in the solar plexus and left her fighting for air. "No!" She couldn't let him do that; she wouldn't. "He's wild and he has a right to stay that way." She looked around for support and found none.

Trent let the silence stretch out thin before he responded. "You kept me from getting my hands on that stallion once before," he said softly, speaking straight at Suzannah. "Way I look at it, this is my second chance and you'll not mess it up again."

"But—"

"I want the stallion and the whole damn herd."

She met his gaze bravely, although he was a hard man to try to face down. "No, Trent. That's wrong. They're wild and belong back on their own range. You can't do this."

"I think I can. I mean to try." He spoke with absolute confidence.

"Now, just a damned minute!" Rex propelled his way into their private confrontation. "Trent, if you think I'm gonna let you keep some mustang stallion around to cause trouble on this range—"

"*Let* me?" Trent thrust out his jaw, almost a reflection of Rex's belligerent expression. "I don't recall askin' your permission, Rex. Besides, once I ride that stud, he won't be wild."

"Okay, I don't think I'm gonna *trust* you to keep some *half*-wild stallion from causin' trouble." Rex sneered. "Because you'll never make a pleasure horse outta him and we both know it." He turned his scorn on his daughter. "As for you, little lady—"

"Don't you 'little lady' me, Pop. You have no right to be deciding the fate of these animals, either of you." She included Trent in her vengeful glance. "The BLM..."

The crowd murmured unhappily. Rex gave a scornful grunt and Trent shook his head with evident disgust.

Suzannah refused to be cowed. "Yes, the BLM! There are laws—"

"And when's the last time anyone served hard time for breakin' laws concerning wild horses?" Rex demanded. "Most of those animals will end up in a can of dog food, anyway, so let's not have any of your bleeding-heart sentiments."

"Ohhh, you make me so blasted mad!" Suzannah stamped her foot. "And you're no better," she accused Trent. "You want to ride bucking horses, go find yourself another rodeo and leave us alone—oh!"

She bit her lip, appalled and thoroughly ashamed of herself for speaking to him that way. He had as much right to be here as she did. She felt even worse when he gave her a surprised glance.

But she hit rock bottom when he laughed.

"Suzannah Glenn, you don't know when to give up," he drawled. "For you, I'm willing to make allowances. But your father..." He scowled at Rex. "If you want a fight you can have one."

"I don't want to fight you, son." Rex looked astonished, as if the thought had never once crossed his mind. "But you start takin' up with wild horses and I'll just naturally have to do something about it." He half turned, adding, "You been gone too long. Guess you've forgotten how things are around here— and where your loyalties lie."

His iron glance swept the circle of men, a pointed reminder of where *their* loyalties better lie, in case any of them had forgotten.

Trent looked just as hard and determined, but before he could respond, Martin Young piped up.

"You're talkin' for all of us, Rex," the little man avowed. "I'd best get on home and tell the missus what's afoot. See you boys tomorrow."

Suzannah stood there feeling helpless while people began to wander away, talking avidly. Her thoughts churned. Pegasus was out there somewhere, she was sure of it, and he was in mortal danger.

"No hard feelin's?"

At her father's words, Suzannah glanced around to find Rex extending his hand to Trent. Trent hesitated, then stuck out his own and the two men shook.

"Come on out to the Monarch anytime," Rex invited, turning on the charm he possessed in somewhat limited amounts. "And if you change your mind about this wild-horse business, we'd be more than happy to have you join us tomorrow."

Trent laughed with apparent good humor. "Rex, when I go lookin' for wild horses, it sure as hell won't be as part of a pack."

"Suit yourself." Rex didn't seem offended. "Just one word to the wise—that stud better be under a saddle or pullin' a plow like an old plug when I catch up to him, because anything less just won't be good enough."

"We'll see, Rex. We sure as hell will."

Again Suzannah sensed the potential for conflict between them. She shivered, looking from one to the other.

Her father wanted the stallion dead, she wanted the stallion free, and Trent wanted the stallion—period.

What chance had she to prevail against two such powerful forces? And then she remembered the wild beauty of the stallion, and her promise to Brittany and Ashley and Jessica.

Suzannah squared her shoulders. Right was on her side. She'd be *damned* if she'd let these two men intimidate her.

CHAPTER THREE

THOROUGHLY OUT OF SORTS, Suzannah walked back into the gym and looked around for Miss Louise. The older woman stood in front of the stage, her hands on her hips and her mouth tight with displeasure.

The musicians had packed up their instruments and were heading for the door, which was just as well. Nobody was thinking of dancing anymore.

Miss Louise greeted Suzannah with a scornfully uttered "Men! They think they're so all-fired important. Send us women off to the kitchen so they can have all the fun, will they? I declare, there's not a one of them with a lick of common sense."

Suzannah blinked in surprise. "My goodness, what's got you all riled up?"

"Your father, who else?" Louise continued to glower. "Rex Glenn has been the bull in this pasture way too long. Somebody needs to take him down a peg or two." Her brown eyes narrowed thoughtfully. "And I might know just the person to do it."

"That doesn't matter now," Suzannah said, impatient to move on to more important subjects. "Miss Louise, what am I going to do? Pop hates wild horses and won't be happy until they'll all dead. Then there's Trent, who apparently wants to catch them just for fun—and to spite Pop. It's ridiculous!"

"You're absolutely right," Miss Louise agreed. "There isn't a reason in the world why we can't all coexist peacefully, man and beast alike. But how are we ever going to convince those two? You tried, and it was like reasoning with a post."

Suzannah groaned. "The problem is I've got to *keep* trying. I promised some terrific little kids I would."

"In that case, you can't afford to stand around wringing your hands. You'd better saddle up and ride out along with everybody else tomorrow." Miss Louise gave her head a sharp affirmative nod. "Men's work—the idea! Forty years ago I'd have given them a real run for their money. Even twenty-five. Now I'm afraid it's up to you, Suzannah."

Two of Suzannah's friends chose that moment to wander over. Anita and Mary Lou did not appear any too happy.

"Looks like the dance is over," Anita said, stating the obvious. "I swear, I don't know why we keep coming to these things, anyway."

Mary Lou gave Suzannah a censorious glance as if it was somehow her fault. "The men are out front talking big and laying plans to track down those wild horses," she said. "You'd think they were invading a foreign country or something."

Anita laughed. "They're all actin' like a bunch of sheep—except Trent. Somebody said he went over to the Lobo to get something to eat." She giggled. "I loved the way he stood up to your father, Suzannah. Would I ever love to see Trent ride that wild stallion!"

"Well, I wouldn't," Suzannah snapped.

Anita raised her eyebrows and exchanged a knowing glance with Mary Lou; both burst into delighted laughter. They obviously thought Jim Trent could do no wrong.

"I'm a little hungry myself," Mary Lou announced. "What say we go to the Lobo and see if Trent needs a little company?"

"Don't mind if we do," Anita concurred. "Lord, that man cleans up good! Want to come along, Suzannah?"

Suzannah shook her head.

"Suit yourself." With a wave, the two ambled out of the gym, all smiles and good humor now.

Suzannah turned back to Miss Louise. "I suppose I'll have to go pull Pop out of that war council," she grumbled.

"Hold off on that a minute."

Suzannah raised her brows in inquiry.

Miss Louise had that determined expression on her face. "I've got a bone to pick with your daddy before you drag him home. Give me a few minutes to speak my piece."

That was fine with Suzannah. She watched Miss Louise march away, thinking she really should go help with kitchen cleanup. When Jim Trent entered through the back door and paused to look around, she knew she should have gone when she had the chance.

She simply wasn't up to another clash of opinions on the subject of wild horses. Glancing about uneasily, she realized that only a few people remained inside the gym and no one was paying her the slightest attention. Quelling a cowardly impulse to run, she watched him approach, noting his slight limp. No wonder, the way he'd been jostled by his admirers, she thought tartly.

She seized the initiative. "I thought you'd gone over to the Lobo to get something to eat and maybe to escape your hoards of admiring fans," she said lightly.

He looked surprised. "I don't know where you got that idea."

"Oh . . . someone mentioned it." She tried for airy disregard, despite a shameful pleasure at the thought of how disappointed Mary Lou and Anita were going to be. She glanced around self-consciously. "Martin Young sure knows how to ruin a party," she said, because that was the first thing that came to mind.

"He's not the only one. Your Pa's no slouch in that department, either." Trent sounded amused and a smile twitched at a corner of his mouth.

That brought reluctant agreement from her. "Pop's rabid when it comes to wild horses. I have no idea why. It's not something he'll talk about, it's just the way he is. You, on the other hand . . ."

"What about me?" His intimate tone sent familiar shivers down her spine.

"You're just borrowing trouble. You don't need those horses, and I'm sure you don't need the grief they'd bring you if you tried to keep them pinned up at the Crazy Ace. My father wouldn't stand for it, Trent. You have to know that."

He cocked his head, regarding her with scarcely contained amusement. "He wouldn't like it much, but that's not of overwhelming importance to me. I'm more interested in the horses themselves. Rex is right about one thing, though, as much as I hate to admit it."

"And that is?"

"If somebody doesn't take responsibility for them, most wild horses end up as dog food—or in a casserole in some country where folks like that sort of thing."

"That's awful!" She cast him a scandalized look. "Eating horse meat? Ugh!"

He grinned. "Not a very cosmopolitan attitude you've got there, Suzy. Just because we don't do it in this country—at least knowingly—doesn't mean there's anything wrong with it. I'll admit I prefer my horses on the hoof, but that's personal prejudice."

"But—"

"Suzy—" suddenly his teasing manner changed, became serious "—make no mistake about it. I want that stallion and I mean to have him. I'd have had him years ago if you hadn't— Well, no use goin' into that again. I never thought I'd get a second chance, but now that I have, I don't plan to blow it—or let you blow it for me."

She stared at him miserably, recognizing raw determination when she saw it. "This is like a bad dream, Trent," she said at last, her voice trembly. "You on one side, my father on the other, and me trying to make both of you see reason. Those horses have a right to be what they are, which is wild. Especially the stallion. He might be better off dead than in captivity. It'd be a crime even to put a rope on him, and what would be the point? You can't teach an old horse new tricks."

"You're wrong, honey. Mustangs can be broken and trained, even old ones." He seemed completely unperturbed. "Most of 'em make damned good working horses. You'll see."

"No, *you'll* see. This horse is different—and don't call me honey." She glared at him, irritated anew by his utter certainty that he was in the right and would prevail. "You and Pop both..." A sudden hope occurred to her. "Or are you doing this just to irritate him? Because if you are, you can accomplish the same thing by taking my side."

Did he hesitate a fraction of a second before answering? "Not a chance."

"While there's life, there's hope," she shot back. Biting her lip, she wondered if there was anything to be gained by throwing herself on his mercy. "Help me!" she burst out, knowing he could, praying he would.

For a long moment he met her gaze and then he sighed. "Sorry. Nice try, but I've got other plans." Touching one finger lightly to his forehead in a quick salute, he left her.

Utterly depressed, she watched him walk away. Was she kidding herself thinking she could make a difference? When he spoke of breaking the stallion to ride, was he seeing the same animal she saw—a wily outlaw who'd just as soon stomp him into the ground as look at him? Would *rather* stomp him into the ground.

At least Trent wasn't out for blood the way most of the ranchers were. The majority of them thought the only good mare-stealing stallion was a *dead* mare-stealing stallion. No one else was going to be too careful about what happened to Pegasus.

Turning the problem over in her mind, she made her way to the kitchen. There she found Brittany's mother wiping pie crumbs off counters.

Linda Daniels looked up with a smile. "Hi, Suzannah. I thought I'd been deserted."

"Not a chance." Suzannah tried to force a cheer she was far from feeling into her tone. "Shall I unplug the coffeepot and clean it?" She nodded toward the big electric urn.

"I'd appreciate that." Linda flipped crumbs into the sink from her dishrag and sighed. "This dance sure went down the drain in a hurry. Too bad about Martin's mare, though."

"Yes." Suzannah unplugged the pot and carried it to the sink, where Linda stepped aside obligingly. Suzannah tipped the pot, pouring out dregs and releasing an aromatic cloud of steam.

Linda watched thoughtfully for a moment, turning the crocheted dishrag between her hands. "Brittany's kind of upset about all this horse business," she said finally. "She and Jessica and some of the other kids have got it into their heads that Pegasus is running around out there in the wild. They're going to be really disillusioned if anything happens to him."

"They won't be the only ones." Suzannah took the brewing basket by the stem and emptied the coffee grounds into the trash can, then faced the other woman. "I'll do what I can, Linda," she said earnestly. "I...sort of promised the kids."

"I know."

"They told you?" Suzannah's heart sank. Any hopes she'd harbored that the children might have forgotten and gone on to some new enthusiasm died on the spot.

Linda looked sympathetic. "It meant a lot to them, Suzannah, but I'm not sure it's a promise you'll be able to keep. I heard what was said out there tonight—everybody did." She shook her head slowly. "Heaven save us from stubborn men."

SUZANNAH FOUND Jenny waiting for Rod near the front door to the gym. "What a night," Jenny groaned. "I thought there for a minute your father and Trent were about to come to blows."

"Maybe they could beat some sense into each other, but I doubt it."

"We should be so lucky." Jenny hesitated. "I don't know about you, but I'm really glad Trent's back to stay. I like him." She wiggled her eyebrows suggestively. "And not just because he's so great-looking, either. He's one of those people who makes things happen—he acts and lets others react. Just being around him is an adventure."

"How much adventure can one town stand?" Suzannah demanded plaintively.

"I think we're about to find out," Jenny predicted. "Besides, anybody who'll stand up to your father is all right in my book—no offense."

"None taken. But has it occurred to you that the only reason Trent is so willing to do that is because he's just as pigheaded as Pop is?"

Jenny sighed. "Actually, that did occur to me, but I figured you'd find a way to get around it." Her glance clearly added, *And what fun to try.*

"Yeah, well, that's not what I wanted to talk to you about," Suzannah said, uncomfortable with the direction the conversation had taken. Somehow she had the feeling that changing Trent's mind would require considerably more in the way of persuasion than she was capable of.

"Then what is?" Jenny glanced around for her date.

Suzannah took a deep breath, letting the tamped-down excitement flare ever so slightly. "I'm going out on my own to look for those wild horses tomorrow,'' she whispered, although there was no one close enough to overhear them. ''How about coming with me?''

Jenny's head snapped back, her dark eyes opening wider. ''You mean it?''

''Sure. I figure I've got an advantage. I know where Trent and I saw them the last time. Everyone else is starting from Martin Young's place, so we'll be ahead of them, if I guess right.''

''So where did you see them the last time?'' Jenny asked. ''I always wondered.''

''You and everybody else. But if I'd told then, the place would have been overrun with would-be mustangers.'' She paused. ''I was trespassing on the Crazy Ace.''

''Shame on you!'' Jenny grinned. ''Being naturally brilliant, it now occurs to me that's why Trent is supporting your story all of a sudden. But since he wants to catch the wild herd himself, won't he head for the same place?''

''Well—'' Suzannah grinned innocently ''—what if he does? As I remember it, Jim Trent was one of the best trackers in the county, and we all know what kind of a roper he is. We could do worse than run into him accidentally-on-purpose.''

Jenny gave a delighted laugh. ''Do you think he'd let us ride with him?''

''He'll have to.'' Suzannah's smile slipped. ''We're the last hope those wild horses have, Jen—scary as that thought may be. I want to be around for whatever happens. And like you said yourself, when you're looking for action, put your money on Trent. So what do you say? Want to go on a mustang-hunt?''

"Sure—why let the guys have all the fun? Let's do it!" Jenny hesitated. "Should I tell Rod? If this turns into a battle of the sexes, I'm not sure we can trust him to go against his own."

"Better not take any chances," Suzannah decided. She leaned closer and lowered her voice. "Okay, here's what we'll do...."

JIM TRENT WATCHED Rex Glenn's pickup pull out of the high-school parking lot. The crown logo of the Monarch Ranch was plainly visible on the passenger door.

As was the passenger herself, when the vehicle passed through pools of light from gymnasium doors and windows. Trent saw Suzannah talking a mile a minute, obviously giving her father hell. He watched until the vehicle and its prickly occupants were out of sight.

But not out of mind. Thinking of Suzannah Glenn, Trent felt a smile tug at the corners of his mouth. She hadn't been pleased by his attitude toward the wild horses, but she would come around eventually. He was, after all, right.

Still smiling, he turned to watch Linda Daniels come through the open door with Miss Louise Addison. Linda was his age, had graduated with his class from Addison High School. She'd been Linda Decker then, but she'd married Tommy Daniels shortly after graduation. He vaguely remembered someone's telling him they had several kids, but he wasn't sure of the details.

He waited while the two women switched off the lights behind them and locked up. When they turned, he said, "Ladies," and lifted his Stetson in a polite greeting.

"Trent." Miss Louise gave him that regal dip of her chin.

Linda flashed him a quick smile.

"Can I offer you ladies a ride home?" he inquired.

Miss Louise declined. "My ride's here," she said, indicating the big Lincoln idling in the parking lot with Winnie behind the wheel. She looked at him, gimlet-eyed. "Jim Trent, you are quite wrong about this wild-horse business. Would there be any point to discussing the matter further at this time?"

"No, ma'am, there surely wouldn't."

"In that case, I'll wish you both a pleasant evening."

Trent watched the old lady leave, filled with admiration. Naturally she would be on Suzannah's side.

He was glad somebody was.

Linda started down the steps. "I'm meeting T.J. at the Lobo," she said. "When he comes here and sees the place dark so early, that's where he'll look next."

"Dance did kinda end abruptly." Trent took her elbow. "I'll walk you over there."

She gave him a startled glance. "You don't need to do that. It's only a block, and this is Addison, after all, not the big city."

"I'll walk you," he repeated, ending any debate. "Besides, I'd like to hear how things are going with you and Tommy. Haven't seen him in a coon's age."

She laughed, giving in to the firm guidance of his hand on her arm. "Nobody's called him Tommy in ten years, Trent. People call him T.J. now. You *have* been gone a long time."

"Maybe too long." They crossed the paved parking lot, heading toward the street. "But now that I'm home to stay, I thought maybe you'd fill me in on what I've missed. For example, Suzannah Glenn..."

THE ARGUMENT with her father, Suzannah finally realized, was getting her nowhere. After a few miles she clammed up and refused further debate.

But as they neared the ranch, she decided she had one more thing to say. "I want your word," she announced, "that you won't hurt those wild horses. Bringing back Martin's mare is one thing, but if that stallion gets hurt there'll be hell to pay, and that's a promise."

"I'm shakin' in my boots." Rex darted her a sarcastic glance, then changed his tactics. "So why do you always blame me?" he demanded plaintively. "What am I, anyway—king of the cowboys? I didn't herd those animals where they don't belong. You can't hold me responsible for every danged wild critter in Wyoming. Things happen, Suzy."

"I've heard *that* song before."

"Well, they do. That bein' the case, are you comin' along with us tomorrow or not?"

"Don't try to change the subject on me."

"I'm not changin' any subject. I don't want you runnin' around out there alone gettin' in the way or gettin' yourself hurt. If you're so all-fired worried about the wild herd and don't trust your old dad, come along and keep an eye on me."

"I trust you," she said sweetly, "as far as I can throw you."

"Then you'll come along?"

"Not a chance."

In the green glow of the instrument panel, she thought he looked relieved. She was perfectly sure he didn't want her along any more than she wanted to be there; his urgings had been nothing but show. Now he could say to her, "But I asked you to come along...."

He didn't fool her for a minute. What he really wanted was for her to stay meekly at home with the women and children. Did she have a surprise for him!

The pickup bounced over the dirt road that would eventually lead them to the ranch house. Rex darted her a cryptic glance. "Think Jim Trent is back to stay this time?"

She shrugged as if she didn't care. "Who knows? He says he is. Apparently he's got big plans for the Crazy Ace."

"Big plans are easy to come by. It's seein' 'em through that takes guts." Rex pulled up in front of the house and killed the engine. "When the goin' gets rough, that boy'll head back to what he knows best—rodeo."

"You think so?" Suzannah felt the knot in her stomach tighten. Her father was putting into words what she'd been thinking all evening.

Rex nodded, a short and sharp punctuation to his words. "Too bad, but it makes no sense, him willin' to give all that up to settle down to a life of hard work on a little ol' piece of ground on the edge of nowhere. Just like his interest in them wild horses, it's a passin' fancy. The boy can ride, there's no doubt about that, but breakin' a bronc and trainin' a hoss to be worth a damn are two different things. One takes flash and the other takes stayin' power."

Suzannah bit her lip, head and spirits drooping. "And you don't think Trent's got staying power?"

"No, darlin', I surely don't." He gave a gusty sigh, redolent with regret. "I'm real sorry to have to say this, but I don't think you oughtta be wastin' your time with him," he added piously. "Not that I don't like him—I do. But you're my girl and I don't want to see you hurt. Jim Trent's a rollin' stone if ever I saw one. He'd only break your heart."

Again he'd put her own thoughts into words, which fell about her like icy drops of rain. Her father, who threw her at every respectable man who came within hailing distance, was warning her against Trent? The implications of this stunned her. He must think Trent was completely out of her league. She felt a little flicker of resentment at the thought.

They climbed out of the pickup and walked up the steps and into the house. Rex switched on a lamp and reached for the remote control to the television.

"Think I'll check the news before I hit the hay," he said, yawning prodigiously. "You sure you don't want to change your mind about tomorrow?"

She shook her head. "I don't see anything to be gained by riding around in circles with a big bunch like that. It'll scare away everything for miles around."

She devoutly hoped so.

"We'll split up, Suzy," he said in a pained voice. "Too bad the plane's been grounded for repairs, but I doubt we'll need it. Me and some of them other ol' boys have chased more wild horses than you'll see in your lifetime. But it's okay with me if you want to stay home and sulk. Just don't blame me later."

Snake oil, nothing but snake oil.

REX AND FOUR of his cowboys drove away from the Monarch Ranch before daybreak Sunday morning.

Suzannah watched through the frilly curtains of her second-story bedroom, then hopped beneath the shower spray. At that point, coherent thought returned—accompanied by excitement.

Perhaps today she'd see Pegasus again. And if her plan worked, Trent would show her the way.

And Jenny, too. Suzannah had deliberately asked Jenny to come along to avoid any kind of intimacy with Trent. Her father, for once, was right.

Trent wasn't the kind of man to bury himself on a little penny-ante ranch like the Crazy Ace. A rolling stone indeed—but he'd never roll over Suzannah Glenn! It did gall her, however, that she'd heard it from her father first.

By the time Jenny arrived, pulling her horse and gear in a trailer behind her brother's pickup truck, Suzannah had everything in readiness. As she led her black gelding up the loading ramp, she saw Jenny suppress a huge yawn.

"I've got to be crazy to do this," Jenny grumbled as Suzannah emerged to slam the tailgate in place. "In all the excitement last night, I forgot to ask a few pertinent questions."

"Such as?" Suzannah hefted her stock saddle and swung it into the bed of the pickup.

Jenny hooked her thumbs in the slash pockets of her pants. Both women were dressed for rough work—jeans, long-sleeved shirts, boots and hats. "Such as, what happens if we find the herd? Neither one of us has much experience mustanging."

"True." Suzannah rubbed her hands in anticipation. "Don't worry. When the time comes, we'll think of something. I heard enough stories from my grandpa that I know *how,* Jen. I just haven't done it yet. It depends on the circumstances. First order of business will be catching Martin's mare—"

"And the second order of business will be getting the wild herd out of the county. Which I, personally, don't think will be possible unless that stallion really is Pegasus and they can all fly."

Suzannah laughed. "You never know," she said lightly. "But there are lots of ways to catch 'em. We may need to build a rope corral, or drive the herd into a box canyon and block the exit. If we're in open country... Well, that's a whole different problem."

Jenny still looked doubtful. "I'm not much of a roper," she confessed.

"Me, either. Chances are, we won't need to be—because Trent is." Suzannah glanced into the bed of the pickup. "Good, you brought your sleeping bag. I've got our chuck, plenty of ropes and incidentals." She gave Jenny a brilliant smile. "Let's hit the trail, cowgirl."

THEY PARKED THE TRUCK and trailer a couple of miles southwest of Wild Horse Creek, far enough away that they wouldn't inhibit the wild herd from watering there. With a minimum of conversation, they unloaded their horses and prepared to move out.

Suzannah had brought Black Jack, a seven-year-old quarter-horse gelding known for good sense and a big heart. Jenny's Tramp was a tall bay mare. Both animals were solid and dependable.

The day sparkled around them like molten gold as they stowed their gear in saddlebags and totes, then strapped everything behind the cantles of their saddles. Sleeping bags followed, secured by saddle strings;

ropes were looped around saddle horns and fastened with leather thongs.

Suzannah stepped back to admire their preparations. "At least our outfit makes us *look* like we know what we're doing," she said with satisfaction.

"Yes, but we know better." Jenny eyed the bulky load while she patted Tramp on the neck. "Think we should have brought a packhorse?" she wondered aloud.

"Maybe," Suzannah conceded. "But I expect we'll be moving too fast to want to bother with one. Besides, if we need anything we don't have, we can drop by one of the line shacks or detour past a ranch house." She gathered her reins. "Ready?"

Jenny squared her shoulders and the two looked at each other. Suzannah began to smile, then Jenny. They were bucking almost the entire county by embarking on what could turn out to be a wild-goose chase or a great adventure. They were as ready for either as they'd ever be.

Tossing the reins over Jack's head, Suzannah leapt lightly into the saddle. The black gelding danced in a circle, eager to be off but responding readily to the guidance of his rider.

"Let's go!" She clapped spurless heels to the horse's sides. Jack sprang forward. Jenny and Tramp followed half a stride behind.

At a steady ground-eating lope, they headed straight for Wild Horse Creek, just inside the boundry of Trent's Crazy Ace. The horses were full of spit and vinegar, and Suzannah's excitement rose with every buoyant stride.

They passed through meadows brilliant with flowers beneath a sky of purest cerulean blue, dotted with fluffy cumulus clouds. A labyrinth of hills rose ahead of them, at the base a line of trees marking the meandering path of the creek.

An antelope bounced up to their right, then veered sharply away. Other than that, not a single living creature could be seen.

Some might call this vast emptiness lonely, but Suzannah called it heaven. Her mother, who'd been born in California, hadn't appreciated much about Wyoming, but she'd particularly disliked the openness—that and the fact that the entire population of the state was fewer than half-a-million permanent residents.

"That's just a mid-size city in California," Kathy Glenn had said shortly before her untimely death. "You ought to see what's out there in the big wide world, Suzannah. Don't you want to go to Disneyland, swim in the ocean, look at the palm trees . . . ?"

Suzannah didn't, and she said so. Everything she'd wanted, then as now, was right here at home.

She shifted in her saddle and waved at Jenny. "This way," she called, reining right toward an outcropping of trees on the banks of the stream.

The time for caution had arrived and they slowed the horses to a walk. Not that Suzannah expected to find Pegasus waiting for them, but if the wild herd had been here, she didn't want to destroy any tracks they might have left.

By the time they reached the edge of the stream, she'd pulled Black Jack down to an amble so she could scan the ground as they passed. So far she'd seen nothing that even vaguely resembled the hoofprint of a horse, but perhaps—

The sound of a man clearing his throat startled her, even though for the past half hour, she'd been almost expecting to run into Trent. Nevertheless, she instinctively pulled on the reins and Jack stopped abruptly, bowing his neck to relieve the pressure of the bit. Suzannah swung around in the saddle, knowing who she'd see but nervous about how he'd react to finding her preparing to trespass on the Crazy Ace yet again.

As she expected, Jim Trent sat his horse on the opposite side of the creek, just as he had that other time. His wrists were crossed over the saddle horn and he waited with perfect ease for her to spot him.

When he saw that she had, he said, very softly and without inflection, "Well, well, well, Miss Glenn—we meet again."

CHAPTER FOUR

SUZANNAH'S HEART gave a funny little leap—simple guilt, she supposed. She released pressure on the reins and gave Trent the most ingenuous smile she could summon. "You scared me," she said.

"No kidding." He straightened in the saddle and used his heels to nudge his horse forward. "Care to tell me what you two're doin' here?"

"We just happened to be in the neighborhood," Suzannah said, tongue in cheek. "Didn't we, Jenny?"

"Oh, absolutely," Jenny agreed on cue. "It's such a beautiful day that Suzannah said to me, 'Jenny, how about driving a truck and trailer with two horses way out in the middle of nowhere and then riding for miles just for the hell of it.' And I said—"

"You should have said it was a dumb idea." Trent guided his horse into the stream. The animal went willingly, the rushing water rising to its knees. Lounging in the saddle, Trent looked every inch the cowboy, even to his well-worn chaps. His mount, going by appearances, was a tough little mustang, not some showy rodeo horse.

There was probably a message there, Suzannah thought, but she ignored whatever it might be and plunged ahead. "Now that we've run into each other, mind if we ride along with you?"

"Ride along with me where?" He halted his horse a few paces in front of them.

"You *are* going to look for Martin's mare, aren't you?"

His grin came lazy and slow. "Well, now, I might at that. Since she's running with the wild herd, it's not too much of a stretch to figure where I'll find her."

"That makes sense." Jenny looked from one to the other. "Doesn't that make sense, Suzannah? Sure is lucky we came along, then. Three heads are better than one, they say."

Suzannah nodded. "Definitely." She gave Trent a cheeky grin. "So what do we do first, partner?"

He chuckled. "Since you're both bein' so friendly, I suppose you think I should share what I've already found—"

"You've already found the herd?" Suzannah blurted. That possibility brought with it not only pleasure but a keen stab of disappointment. Not that she'd wanted to spend the next few days in close proximity with this man, of course.

"I found their trail, and it's on my land." He nodded toward the hills. "I guess I don't mind sharing that information with . . . friends."

Friends? She swallowed hard. "That's us, all right," she agreed brightly.

Jenny nudged her horse forward a few steps, stopping between them. She looked from one to the other, her glance puzzled. "So don't just sit here trying to stare each other down. Let's go find us some horses."

TRENT SHOWED THEM the tracks he'd located on the banks of the stream. Dismounting, the three of them knelt for a closer examination.

It looked like nothing more than a muddy trample to Suzannah, until Trent reached out to touch a sharp ridge in the earth.

"The stallion made these," he said with satisfaction. "See, some prints are much deeper, made by a bigger animal. He reared up here—these tracks are deeper still. Something disturbed him."

Suzannah felt a flare of alarm. "Not any of the search parties, surely. They couldn't be ahead of us, could they?"

Trent shook his head. "It wasn't a man scared him—it was a big cat. I found sign over there." He gestured to a clump of trees growing nearer the water. "This stallion's a smart one. Didn't let any of his mares get close enough for the cat to do any damage."

Jenny gave him an admiring look. "I don't see how you can tell all that just by glancing at a piece of ground that looks like it's been trampled by a herd of buffalo," she said. "It's sure a good thing we met up with you."

"It doesn't take an experienced tracker to see that the band took off in that direction," Suzannah objected. She pointed toward the faint trail leading away from the stream.

Trent brushed his palms across the rough leather of his chaps. "Right you are. That's a well-established path and they took it. But it only goes as far as those foothills, and what do you do then, Calamity Jane?"

She gave him a sweet smile. "Then I turn to the big strong cowboy and holler help!"

Trent laughed and shook his head in mock surrender. "And the big strong cowboy's gonna fall for it, sure as hell."

Jenny jumped to her feet and grabbed her saddle horn, preparing to mount.

"And where do you think you're going?" Trent inquired.

"After the herd, of course."

He shook his head. "Not so fast. First we destroy or mess up the tracks the wild herd left here and *then* we go after them. No need hanging out a sign for the folks who'll come after us."

And so they did. First they rode their own horses back and forth over the ground where the herd had watered until they'd obliterated all tracks of unshod animals. Then, using a leafy tree branch, Trent carefully swept away tracks leading to the trail.

Finally they rode upstream until they reached a scrubby section of bank where they could turn east without leaving a trail. Thus it was well past noon before they again struck the course of the wild herd. By that point, Trent was satisfied they no longer needed to fear being tracked themselves.

They stopped for a late lunch at the edge of as pretty a little meadow as Suzannah had ever seen. Ablaze with yellow and purple wildflowers, it was ringed by wooded gentle-looking hills that she knew wouldn't be quite so gentle when they tried to ride over them.

Opening her saddlebags, Suzannah withdrew a sack of sandwiches and plucked her canteen strap from around the saddle horn. Squirrels scolded from high atop lofty conifers, and a ground squirrel bobbed up and down in the grass nearby, shrill in his displeasure.

She served cheese sandwiches all around, along with handfuls of carrot sticks. "How far ahead do you think the horses are?" she asked Trent.

He looked thoughtfully at his sandwich. "A ways," he said finally. "They're not in any great hurry—at least, not yet. They're just meanderin' along, grazing as they go. Once they realize we're back here it'll be a different story."

"Do you—" Suzannah swallowed back the impatience burning in her throat "—think this is the right bunch? I mean the bunch led by the white stallion that stole Martin's mare?"

"It's the right bunch," Trent said flatly.

"How can you be so sure when we haven't even caught a glimpse of them?"

"Easy." He finished his sandwich and rolled the waxed paper into a small ball before thrusting it into a pocket in his jeans. "They're all barefoot except for two of 'em. Martin Young's mare is one, and the other's a mare that was taken some time back. She's got a shoe nearly worn away on her left front hoof, and a broken partial on the right."

Jenny's eyes grew huge with admiration. "Wow!" she breathed. "You can tell all that just from the tracks?"

Trent grinned and his eyes crinkled at the corners. "I can tell more than that. Every living critter leaves sign of some sort. The trick's in the readin'."

Suzannah wished he hadn't been looking at her when he said that. She couldn't imagine what he might be "reading" in her face, but whatever it was made him smile.

And his smile sent a shiver up her backbone.

AFTER LUNCH, they rode on into the foothills with Trent leading the way. Directly behind him, Suzannah found herself watching the man, instead of her surroundings. She always felt a deep contentment in Wyoming's pristine wilderness, but this time all she felt was a tension that grew more pronounced with every mile.

As a tracker and outdoorsman, Trent was everything she remembered, right down to the easy confidence that could never be called arrogance or conceit. She remembered him as good and found him better.

She remembered him as sexy and found him sexier.

But in other ways, he seemed the same, although she couldn't believe he really was. Ten years ago he'd been an unsophisticated cowboy, but since then he'd seen the elephant, as her grandpa would have said—he'd seen the world. He'd won fame and adulation and earned a great deal of money.

Yet here he was, dressed in faded work clothes like any other cowboy, leading the search for a band of wild horses. She recognized his bone-deep satisfaction in the chase, too, because it so nearly matched her own.

But what would happen when they found the herd? He wanted one thing, she another, and neither would retreat.

Trent twisted in the saddle and gave her a quick smile, pointing to the side of the trail. She whipped her head around just in time to see a pronghorn antelope slip away through the trees.

He shrugged and turned back. His horse moved on a loose rein, steps almost dainty in their precision. She kicked Black Jack up until she could ride beside him. It was silly to feel so self-conscious with this man.

"That's a nice little horse you're riding," she said, knowing that the surest way to make points with a cowboy was to compliment him on his choice of horseflesh. "A mustang, or I miss my guess."

"That's right." He did look pleased. "You send a mustang to catch a mustang."

"That's what my grandpa used to say." She leaned forward to pat her own horse on the neck. "Black Jack here's a quarter horse and a good one, but he's had to step out to keep up with your little gelding."

"Well," Trent drawled, "you know how a mustang is—tough and wild and ornery as hell. You can't let your guard down with one of 'em for a minute."

She returned his smile, but she was thinking, *You're a mustang, too, Jim Trent.* It'd probably be easier to tame the white stallion than this man—and the stallion, she was quite sure, would be impossible.

The faint trail they followed opened into another tiny hidden meadow. Jenny trotted up on Trent's other side, and they rode three abreast.

"Are we gaining on them?" Jenny asked.

Trent nodded. "But we won't catch up with 'em tonight." He nodded toward the west. "Sun'll be dropping behind those mountains in another couple of hours, and we'll have to find us a spot to bed down." A smile flicked at the corner of his lips. "You ladies did come prepared to spend a night or two on the range, I presume."

Jenny nodded, although she didn't look all that eager. "And food." She rose in her stirrups and looked around. "You got any idea where we are, Trent?"

"Sure do. I've explored all these hills, one time or another. When I was a kid—" He stopped short, giving Suzannah a sheepish grin. "You weren't the only one who used to trespass on the Crazy Ace. Yeah, I got the lay of the land around here. Probably not as well as that white stallion up there but—''

"You've seen him?" In her excitement, Suzannah leaned over and grabbed his arm. At the bolt of awareness that shot through her, she quickly yanked her hand away. "Oh, Trent, you've seen him? Why didn't you say so? When?"

"I didn't see him, but I did find this."

Holding out his left hand, clenched in a fist, he slowly uncurled the fingers. She leaned forward, filled with excitement. A few white hairs rested on his palm. At that moment a puff of wind passed by, wafting the hairs away with the breeze.

She frowned at him, not understanding.

He explained. "I found a tuft of white hair stuck to a bush back there when I got down to check sign. I've got a gut feeling . . ."

He paused, a faraway look in his blue eyes as if he could see past the hills ringing them in. "It's him, Suzannah. As sure as God made little green apples, it's your Pegasus out there."

"He's not *my* Pegasus. He's not anybody's Pegasus." But she couldn't resist twisting around with one hand on the cantle and the other on the saddle horn to stare down the trail behind her, as if she could conjure back the silvery hairs. Touching them would be almost like touching the animal, she thought, feeling the loss out of all proportion.

"If you don't claim him, we'll just call him *my* Pegasus, then," Trent said. "Look, I know a place we can camp. Good water, good graze for our horses. It's still a couple of hours away, so it's time we quit loafin' along."

He lifted the reins and the mustang sprang forward. Trent rode like a centaur, Suzannah thought as she urged Black Jack into a short lope. An image of Jim Trent astride the wild white stallion flashed across her mind, and she caught her breath. What a contest of man against beast that would be!

Not that such a clash of wills would ever take place, if she had anything to say about it. There would be one winner and one loser in such a showdown. She couldn't bear the thought of either man or horse humbled.

Jenny galloped past on Tramp. "Wake up, sleepyhead!" she shouted, clapping heels to the mare's sides as they pulled away.

With a grimace, Suzannah pulled her attention back where it belonged and followed.

THEY MADE CAMP in a clump of cottonwoods near a bend in a small creek Suzannah hadn't even known existed.

"It's called Little Dry Branch," Trent explained as he unsaddled his horse. "That's to distinguish it from the Big Dry."

Suzannah couldn't help teasing. "Both of which must be distinguished from Big and Little Wet Branches, right?"

Trent shrugged and grinned, his square even teeth flashing against his sun-darkened skin. "Give the pretty lady a cigar," he drawled.

"You're both crazy," Jenny declared, dragging the heavy saddle off Tramp's back. The tall bay mare shivered with pleasure.

Suzannah *felt* crazy, or maybe giddy was a better word for it. She'd spent most of the day staring at

Trent's broad back while she fought the hypnotic power of imagination. She had to admit that the strain was getting to her.

"Tell you what." Trent smiled at her. "I'll finish unsaddling the horses and hobble them in the meadow where they can graze if the two of you want to start setting up camp."

He reached out just as Suzannah grabbed for the horn to pull the saddle off Black Jack's back. His hand covered hers, his fingers curving down possessively.

She stiffened, her surprised gaze flying to his face. He grinned, a wicked, wicked grin that set teasing lights to dancing in his eyes.

Then just as suddenly her hand was free, and she thought perhaps she'd imagined the possessiveness, that it had been nothing more than an accidental touch. Feeling gauche about the whole thing, she watched him haul the saddle off her horse with one hand. Hefting it, he tossed it on the ground beneath the trees.

She'd been the victim of an overactive imagination, she decided, absently rubbing her tingling hand beneath the opposite elbow. But then he turned toward her, and the satisfied curve of his lips brought a hot wave of indignation crashing over her.

Darn you, Jim Trent, she thought, picking up her sleeping bag and provisions before marching away. He was playing games with the little country girl, that was all. He knew as well as she did that they were on a collision course over those wild horses.

If he thought he was going to get around her by playing up to her, he darn well had another think coming.

IT WAS LIKE A PAGE out of the past, setting up camp, cooking supper over a campfire, spreading the bedrolls. Suzannah kept an eye on Trent while she worked, her tension growing and expanding until she felt almost as if she was holding her breath, waiting for something to happen.

She had no idea what—or if she did, refused to let it form images or even words in her mind. Trent moved back and forth between the camp, the horses and the creek, and her awareness of him continued to expand. By the time they sat down to eat, she was a nervous wreck.

There was little dinner conversation at first, for all three were hungry from the day's activities and light rations at noon. Night settled around them and the stars came out before the meal was finished.

Trent was the last to put aside his tin plate. He stretched, then leaned back on the log that defined that side of the camp. The small fire leapt and crackled in the center of the clearing.

"Good chuck," he announced.

Jenny giggled and darted a glance at Suzannah. "I've always said that no one has a way with a can of chili like Suzannah."

Suzannah laughed in relief. There had been something so intimate in that silence she was glad to have it broken. "Jenny put the cheese on the crackers. Don't give me all the credit." She sighed and tilted her head back so she could stare up at the stars. "Don't you love it out here at night?" she asked rhetorically. "Don't you feel closer to God somehow?"

"Nope." But Jenny, too, looked up at the sky with apparent appreciation. "I used to want to do this kind of pioneer thing when I was a kid. Now that I'm all grown up, though, I must admit a certain fondness for the comforts of home.''

Trent smiled lazily. ''Then you're a helluva good sport to let Suzy talk you into coming out here like this.''

Jenny looked alarmed. ''She lets you call her *Suzy?* I thought that was a shooting offense.''

''It is.'' Suzannah pretended to glower at him because it was expected of her, but she found it difficult to maintain the pretense. She gave it up somewhat sheepishly. ''You,'' she said to Trent, ''are incorrigible.''

His mouth curved up at one corner and he winked at Jenny. ''Last person to call me incorrigible was my sixth-grade teacher, Miss Maxwell. She didn't understand, either.''

''Understand what?'' Jenny sat up, her eyes bright with interest.

Trent looked at Suzannah. ''That sometimes there's just no room for compromise. Call me stubborn—''

Suzannah laughed. ''Now who'd do a thing like that?''

''Call me stubborn,'' he repeated with a smile, ''but if there's a wild white stallion still out there somewhere, he's *mine.*'' An almost palpable tension electrified the air. ''Damn, do you women have any idea how long men have been chasing that animal?''

''Yes,'' Suzannah said.

''No,'' Jenny contradicted. When Suzannah frowned, she added, ''Well, I don't. I know the Pegasus myth—white horse with wings and all—but that's it. What's the deal on the white stallion, anyway?''

Trent leaned forward, propping his forearms on his knees. In the firelight, his face took on an almost mystical glow.

"He's been known by a lot of different names—the White Stallion of the Plains, the Pacing White Stallion, the White Mustang, Ghost Horse of the Plains— but in every story he's the fastest, best lookin', wildest son of a gun ever seen by mortal man. Since the early 1800s, he's been reported from Mexico to Canada and all points in between."

Caught up in the story, Suzannah nodded. "Washington Irving—"

"*The* Washington Irving?" Jenny inserted.

Suzannah nodded. "In the early 1830s Washington Irving wrote about a wild white horse that could pace faster than ordinary horses could run. A few years later, there were newspaper reports about a wild white horse in Texas that they called the White Steed of the Prairies—another pacer, able to avoid the wiliest mustangers riding racehorses."

Jenny glanced from one to the other. "Is this one a pacer, do you suppose?"

"I don't know." Suzannah turned to Trent for guidance.

"No," he said. When Suzannah and Jenny looked surprised, he added, "Well, he's not—I can tell from the tracks. But not all the stories of the white stallion call him a pacer. What all the stories have in common is his speed and intelligence."

"And beauty," Suzannah added. "And love of freedom. Not a single one of those stories claimed he'd ever been caught and tamed. In fact, in some versions he threw himself off a cliff or even drowned himself before submitting." She looked at Trent accusingly.

"Hey," he said lightly, "they're only tall tales, right? But like Suzannah, I've heard 'em since I was a kid. She heard 'em here in Wyoming, but I heard the same stories in Texas, before I ever moved here. And like every red-blooded boy, I dreamed of being the one cowboy smart enough and tough enough to catch and tame that white horse."

"Most boys grow up and move on to other dreams eventually," Suzannah suggested, meeting his gaze squarely.

"Not if they're lucky enough to know the dream's still out there somewhere to be had," he said softly. "Suzy, that day I caught you skinny-dippin' in Wild Horse Creek—"

Jenny choked on astonished laughter, but neither paid her the slightest attention, intent as they were on each other.

"—I also saw the horse I'd dreamed of since I was a kid. The whole thing happened awful quick, but there was something so—" he licked his lips and drew an exasperated breath, as if words suddenly failed him "—so *preordained* about the whole thing. It was meant to be. I was supposed to have that horse, but you scared him away."

"If that's true, I wouldn't have been there," she argued. "Or you'd have caught him, anyway, despite anything I might have done. I've thought about it, too—a lot. I've concluded that we were very, very lucky. Not many people get to see a legend, Trent. Why would you want to kill it?"

She tried to keep her tone light, but her mouth had gone dry. She reached for her tin cup and poured water from her canteen.

"I don't want to kill the legend—I want to own it," he said bluntly. "You're all caught up in some romantic do-gooder fantasy, Suzy. I'm chasing a flesh-and-blood animal, and when I catch him..." He shrugged.

"You're crazy if you think you can tame him," she cried, "even if you do somehow manage to get your hands on him."

For a moment Trent strained forward. Then all the tension seemed to drop away and he leaned back against the log again, his expression masked by shifting shadows. "You can teach an old horse new tricks, honey."

"You're wrong. Not when the old horse has run wild for more than ten years—and don't call me honey."

"Sure, Suzy, anything you say." He plucked a brand from the campfire and examined the glowing tip. "A horse is a horse. There're good ones and bad ones but they're still all horses. That's reality—and reality rarely measures up to fantasy."

"No," she snapped, "sometimes it's better!" She clenched her hands into fists. "Where did you get the idea I'm some little nitwit who doesn't know the difference between fantasy and reality? I've got my feet planted more firmly on the ground than you do, Jim Trent. I'm interested in doing the right thing to help real animals. You...you're just being selfish."

Trent stared at her for a moment as if she were a different species entirely. Then he stood and tossed the stick back into the flames. Without another word, he walked off into the darkness.

Jenny whistled under her breath, a long low exclamation. "Holy cow," she muttered. "What just happened here?"

For some reason, Suzannah felt like crying. She bit her lower lip until it stopped trembling and then shook her head helplessly. "I—I don't really know," she admitted. "I'm not even sure what we were talking about—wild horses, Trent, or me."

Jenny said nothing. Surprised, Suzannah turned to find her friend staring at the fire with a pensive expression.

"Jenny? You all right?"

"Sure, I'm fine. Trent may not understand, but I do. You told him the truth—you're a levelheaded, sensible woman. So am I, and yet... when you love somebody, or something... well, you don't always think as clearly as you should."

"You're talking about Rod now," Suzannah guessed.

"I suppose I am. Silly of me, I know. He's not at all what I want in a man. He's not ambitious, he's not very romantic, he took me for granted before I ever even agreed to go out with him. Jeez!" She jumped up and dusted off the seat of her jeans. "I'm too smart a woman to fall for a man like that."

Yeah, right—you and who else? Suzannah wondered, watching Jenny bustle around, cleaning up after the meal.

After a few minutes, she got up wearily to help.

CHAPTER FIVE

SUZANNAH LAY in her sleeping bag and stared up at the star-studded bowl of the Wyoming sky. Somewhere a coyote howled, but rather than making her feel lonely, it offered a kind of comfort. A few feet away, Jenny's deep breathing indicated she'd found the sleep that had thus far eluded Suzannah.

Heaven knew she needed all the comfort she could find, from whatever source. Conflicting feelings about Jim Trent had left her a veritable mass of confusion.

The crunch of bootsteps sent warning ripples through her, even though—or perhaps, because—she knew who it was. Trent was making his way to his bed on the opposite side of the small clearing.

She bit her lip, considering. Then she took a quivering breath and said his name, very low and ending on a question.

All sound instantly ceased. After a moment, he walked to where she lay and stood over her.

"Suzy? You awake?"

"Yes." She darted a glance toward the sleeping mound that was Jenny. "Could I...talk to you for just a minute?"

"Sure." He bent his long legs to hunker down beside her, a darker silhouette against a dark sky. "What's up?"

"N-nothing." She shifted in her sleeping bag, wondering if he could see her better than she could see him. And hoping he couldn't. "I've been thinking..."

"Yes?"

"Tomorrow we should find the wild herd and it just seems to me...well, we're going to have to reach some compromise, whether we want to or not."

"Yes?"

He wasn't helping her even a little. "What I said earlier... I hope I didn't offend you."

He laughed, a low warm chuckle. "I've got a thicker hide than that." He hesitated for a moment, then went on, "Besides, I deserved a dressing down. I know you're not some little nitwit who doesn't know reality from fantasy. But about compromise—it sounds good in theory, but I don't see anyplace in the middle where we can meet except..."

A faint hope sparked inside her. "Except?"

"Well, if we get down to the point where it's either my way or your father's, I expect my way will look pretty good to you. According to your pa, the only good wild horse is a dead wild horse, and I don't imagine that sets any too well with you."

"No, but—"

"Suzy, it all depends on how bad you want a thing and what you got to prove. I want that white stallion in the worst way."

"But you don't have anything to prove," she argued. "Even I realize you can break him if you really set your mind to it—assuming you can catch him without killing him in the process."

"Yeah, right." He sounded disgusted for some reason. "Let's turn that around. What do you have to prove?"

She considered carefully, trying to be honest. "I guess...just that I'm willing to stand up for what I believe."

"Okay, you've already done that. You've stood up for it and lost. No disgrace there."

"You didn't let me finish. I also gave my word to some great kids that harm would come to those wild horses only over my dead body." She gave a rueful little laugh. "I'm too young to die, Trent!"

"That," he said with unexpected feeling, "is the damned truth."

He lightly trailed the fingers of one hand over her cheek. She caught her breath and lay perfectly still, trying with all her might to pierce the darkness to see his expression.

He touched her lips with seductive fingertips. She closed her eyes on a languid sigh. She felt hot and cold at the same time; hopeful and frightened all at once.

"Damn," he muttered, his hand sliding into the tousled thickness of her hair. "This is a helluva bad idea."

He withdrew his hand so suddenly that her head bounced on her pillow, which was only a rolled-up towel. He rose, his movements uncharacteristically jerky. "Go to sleep," he said roughly. "We're gonna have a hard day tomorrow."

He walked away, limping a little. She closed her eyes tightly, breathing in quick shallow pants. She'd accomplished nothing, nothing—except to expose herself to more of his particular brand of sensual charm. *Don't think about that, don't think about that,* she warned herself. *Don't wonder about what he meant when he said this was a bad idea.*

She concentrated upon interpreting his movements by sound: when he sat down on the log, when he tugged off his boots, when he lowered himself with a ragged sigh into his waiting bedroll.

She and Jenny had brought nylon sleeping bags, but Trent had opted for an honest-to-goodness old-time bedroll. They'd watched him unfurl it with considerable curiosity.

Aware of their interest, he'd smiled. "Ace Kilmer taught me to do this," he'd explained. "It's what the old-timers called a roundup bed. You start with a good tarp..."

As he spoke, he showed them the various layers, beginning with a tarpaulin of heavy waterproof ducking on the bottom, followed by "soogans"—the old-time cowboy's name for quilts. Cotton blankets went on top; then the tarp was folded over on the sides and laced together with snaps and rings to keep everything in place.

He tossed a small drawstring bag where his head would eventually rest. "When you get all your possibles in your 'war bag,' it makes a right good pillow," he explained.

Suzannah frowned. "Why, Trent? That's fascinating, doing it the old way. But it's so much more trouble, and it sure doesn't look any more comfortable."

For a moment she thought he wasn't going to answer her, but then he straightened and turned slowly. "I...don't really know, Suzy. Maybe to see if I remembered how, or maybe to see if I can get back to a place I haven't been for a very long time." He shrugged. "Maybe I'm just trying to recreate a way of life that's gone. I honestly don't know."

Remembering his faintly wistful tone, she shivered in her own high-tech bed, although the night was mild and pleasant. Jim Trent was a mystery she dared not try to unravel. He was out of her league. Better to spend the dark and quiet hours counting sheep than listening to the deep even breathing of a man she would never begin to understand.

SHE AWOKE in that first uncertain light, caught somewhere between day and night. The fire had long since burned itself out. For a moment she snuggled deeper into her cozy cocoon.

Then she remembered where she was and why. Sitting bolt upright, she clenched her hands into fists. Today they should catch up with the wild herd.

Moving silently to avoid disturbing the others, she crawled out of her sleeping bag. She grabbed the small canvas tote holding what Trent would call her possibles and crept quietly through the trees to the low banks of the little stream. Kneeling, she dug around and pulled out washcloth, toothpaste and toothbrush.

Today would tell the story, she promised herself while she washed her face with water so cold it sent a shiver down her spine. With any luck, they'd have surprise on their side. Trent had explained last night that once the horses knew they were being trailed, they'd be that much more cautious and difficult to fool.

The first chance would therefore be the best chance—maybe even the last chance.

Squirting toothpaste onto her brush, she cleaned her teeth with automatic strokes. If they could spot the horses before the horses spotted them, they might be able to come up with a feasible plan. They'd have to play it by ear, Trent had said. It would all depend ...

Cupping her hands, Suzannah leaned over the creek to rinse toothpaste from her mouth. For some reason, she had supreme confidence that the wild herd was nearby and that today she'd come face-to-face with Pegasus—while at the same time, finding a way to keep him out of Trent's clutches.

Smiling with anticipation, she lifted her head and a chill shot through her.

She *was* face-to-face with the white stallion. He stood no more than thirty feet away, on the far side of Little Dry, head up and nostrils flaring. Gilded by the sun rising behind him, he *did* look like a dream, and more magnificent than she had ever conjured up even in her wildest imaginings.

Did he see her? She dared not move, dared not breathe. Crouched as she was near the trunk of a tree, he might not yet be aware of her presence, assuming the wind was in the right direction. *Oh, Lord, what should she do?*

The rest of the herd crowded up behind and around the stallion, and Suzannah realized belatedly that she and Pegasus were not alone. He snorted and took a tentative step into the water, the red-and-gold rays of the sun glinting off his silver hide.

Something disturbed him and he threw his head up and arched his neck, although Suzannah was absolutely certain she hadn't made a sound. She wasn't even breathing, for heaven's sake, and the effort was making her light-headed.

Then she heard it, too: the soft snuffle of a horse somewhere behind her. Jenny's mare must have attracted the stallion, ever eager for a new conquest.

He walked a few paces into the flowing water, his gaze going right past the woman lurking in the shadow of a tree. His ears pricked forward with an interest so intense she could almost feel it. His harem milled around behind him, drinking and getting in one another's way, but he paid them no mind. He had a new prize to win.

But something went wrong. Suzannah had no idea what; she didn't hear a thing beyond the ordinary morning sounds of birds and insects and creaking tree limbs. In an instant the entire herd was in a frenzy of activity, moving this way and that, poised to run, turning to run—right toward her.

She knew in a flash that she was perfectly safe if she stayed crouched beside the tree. But in that same flash she realized something else: the herd was about to stampede directly toward the camp where Jenny and Trent probably still slept.

Without hesitation, Suzannah bolted to her feet and threw herself into the path of the rampaging herd, yelling at the top of her lungs.

JIM TRENT, sitting his horse at a small knoll on the edge of the trees on the west side of the creek, had no idea Suzannah wasn't still in her sleeping bag until she burst out of the trees and into the path of the stampeding horses. With a sharp curse lost in the thunder of hoofbeats, he jammed blunted spurs into his horse's ribs.

The animal exploded forward and in three strides bore down on the woman from behind. Her sudden appearance had thrown the wild horses into further turmoil, which gave Trent time to lean sideways in the saddle and pluck her from harm's way. He deposited her on the saddle before him none too gently.

But that left him no opportunity to get out of the path of the horses charging across Little Dry Branch, water spraying from flashing hooves. Clutching Suzannah against his chest, Trent deftly reined his mount between the rushing bodies. The white stallion passed so close that his shoulder actually brushed Suzannah's foot.

Emerging on the far bank, Trent spun his horse in a tight circle to stare after the retreating herd. Suzannah stirred in his arms, realized where she was and jerked upright. He ignored her struggles to dismount, instead lifting the reins to guide his horse back across the creek.

"Darn you, Jim Trent!" She brought one fist down on his chest, still trying to escape his iron grip. "Martin's mare is getting away! Don't just sit here—do something!"

All the fear he'd felt for her safety boiled up. Deliberately tightening his hold, he glared at her. "What the hell do you think you were doing back there, jumping into the path of a stampede like that? You could have been killed!"

She flinched before his anger, her beautiful sherry-colored eyes flying wide. Instead of looking contrite or grateful, her chin rose another notch. "Don't be ridiculous. I wasn't in any *real* danger. I was just trying to head them away from camp. I was afraid you and Jenny were still asleep and—"

"Jenny's awake and showed a helluva lot more sense than you did. She shinned up a tree."

"I didn't know that, did I?" Again she tried to shrug out of his hold. "Let me go!"

"What, no word of thanks?" Still furious with her, he yanked his arm more tightly around her waist.

"You want thanks? All right—thanks! Thanks for nothing!"

Staring into that unrepentant face, Trent growled in frustration. Suzannah Glenn was the orneriest, stubbornest, most pigheaded...beautiful, desirable woman he'd ever encountered. Last night she'd tempted him, but he'd stood firm. Today...well, today was something else again. Today danger had torn down his defenses.

"Suzy—" he began in an exasperated tone.

"And don't call me Suzy!" She stopped struggling and stared straight at him, her soft pink mouth set in an obstinate line.

Trent's control, severely tested since he'd run afoul of Suzannah Glenn more than a decade ago, finally snapped. Hauling her hard against his chest, he did the one thing he knew he shouldn't. He kissed her.

HIS LIPS TOUCHED HERS and time stood still for Suzannah. With a soft murmur of surprised delight, she threw her arms around his neck and kissed him back.

Oh, dear, she thought hazily, *kissing him is every bit as wonderful as I thought it would be.* Maybe more so, for unreasonable as his anger was, it added a special urgency to the way he touched her and held her.

Where that torrid kiss might have led nobody would ever know, for a shrill shriek shattered the moment.

"Suzannah, Trent—I saw him! Omigosh, he's real! The white stallion's real! I saw him!"

Trent pulled back with a muttered oath. Suzannah turned her head groggily toward Jenny's excited shouts. Belatedly realizing how quickly and completely she'd yielded to him, she gathered her scattered wits enough to push herself out of his arms.

This time he not only let her go, he helped her slide down the horse's shoulder until her feet touched the ground. She nearly fell. Reaching out to brace herself, her groping hand touched his hard thigh, instead of the horse's neck. She jerked her hand away quickly, giving Trent a censorious glance.

On wobbly knees, she took a step toward Jenny, who skidded to a halt and pointed in the direction the horses had disappeared.

"Go after them!" Jenny shrieked. "Oh, Trent, go after them and catch Martin's mare! Then Mr. Glenn and his vigilantes won't have any more excuses."

Trent's horse danced in a circle, but he held the animal back. "Calm down—I'm going. The two of you break camp and then follow me. I'll leave clear sign so you can't get lost."

"We're not stupid," Suzannah declared. "We'll find you. Just don't forget—we're after the mare, not the stallion. Go, will you, before they get clean away!"

The look he gave her clearly indicated that as far as he was concerned, the jury was still out on the question of "stupid." Touching the brim of his hat lightly with two fingers, he spun his horse and touched spurs to the animal's sides.

Suzannah scrubbed her mouth with the back of one hand while she watched them gallop away. Aroused and excited and confused, she hardly knew which emotion to deal with first.

Jenny grabbed Suzannah's hand and dragged her toward camp. "I saw him!" she crowed. "I saw the white stallion, just like you described him last night. It was thrilling!"

It had thrilled Suzannah, too. She shivered, remembering how she'd felt when she first looked up and saw that magnificent animal standing before her in all his glory and mystery.

Jenny's voice dropped. "I saw something else, too. I saw Trent kiss you."

Suzannah groaned. "That wasn't a kiss, it was a...a reprimand! He was mad at me."

"Maybe, but don't kid yourself—it was still a kiss. You two are really...powerful together."

It was true, they were. Suzannah slumped onto her sleeping bag, propped her elbows on her knees and let her head sink into her hands. "He's too much like my father," she said miserably. "There's no give in him. He doesn't seem to realize that I'm as determined to have my way about the wild horses as he is to have his."

Jenny began to roll up her sleeping bag. "You haven't exactly offered him a compromise, have you? Be reasonable, Suzannah, he—"

"I don't have to be any more reasonable than he does! A wild horse can't be half-broken or half-free, Jen—or half-dead, if you want to include my father's preference."

"Then what we have here is a no-win situation, I'm afraid." Jenny finished securing her sleeping bag and moved on to Trent's bedroll. "Unless you can think of something Trent wants even more than he wants that horse."

"Such as?" Suzannah scooted off her sleeping bag and began to reassemble it for rolling. "What could I possibly offer him that could compare with— Oh."

What she saw in Jenny's arch expression was so ridiculous that she glared her outrage. "I wouldn't sleep with a man I didn't love if he hung the stars and the moon," she declared. "I'll admit Trent . . . appeals to me. . . ."

"A lot," Jenny supplied.

"Well, sure, a lot. But simple attraction isn't enough. Not nearly enough."

"Okay, just checking." Jenny threw items into saddlebags, moving quickly. "Are you about ready to go? I'd hate for him to get too far ahead of us."

Suzannah grabbed the cooking utensils and stuffed them into the folds of Trent's bedroll, then ran to get her horse. Action was just what she needed to take her mind off Trent's kiss.

IT TOOK SUZANNAH and Jenny no more than twenty minutes to strike camp, saddle up and set out on Trent's trail. But it was noon before they saw him riding back toward them through a grassy meadow.

Kicking up their horses, they met in the middle.

"What are you doing here?" Suzannah demanded. "Did you lose the herd?"

Trent shook his head. He looked relaxed and confident. "They're up ahead a couple of miles. They've settled down to graze, so I took a chance and came on back to see if you two were behind me. Glad to see you made it."

Suzannah lifted her chin. "Why shouldn't we?" She hoisted his saddlebags from her horse's withers and handed them over. "We didn't just fall off a hay wagon, you know."

Jenny's laughter held a nervous edge. "Don't squabble, children. We're here about horses, remember?"

Trent grinned. "Right you are. How about a quick bite to eat while I tell you my plan."

Suzannah's anxiety fell away. "You've got a plan? That's wonderful!"

He explained while they ate—cheese and crackers, followed by chocolate-chip cookies, washed down with water from their canteens—since he judged them too close to the horses to risk a fire. What he had in mind was simple enough.

He would circle around and station himself at a bottleneck on the other side of the valley where the horses grazed. At a prearranged time, the women would move up to drive the herd toward him. He'd depend on his rope and the spares Suzannah and Jenny had handed over—the luck of a few quick tosses.

Suzannah breathed a sigh of satisfaction. "It'll work," she said. "I know it will. And once Martin gets his mare back, things in Addison should quiet down."

Trent gave her a crooked little grin. "Thanks for your faith. But understand, we'll be putting all our eggs in one basket. I can only count on this one quick shot at 'em. Once they pass through that bottleneck they'll be home free. It's rugged country back there."

"All we need is one shot," Suzannah said, supremely confident in his ability with a rope and trying to be equally confident that his target would be the mare, not the stallion.

Jenny nodded. "So let's synchronize our watches," she suggested, thrusting out her wrist. She grinned. "I've always wanted to say that!"

TRENT LAY in the sunny meadow on his back, his booted feet crossed at the ankle, his arms bent to pillow his head. He'd pulled his Stetson low over his eyes. He'd been lying there for perhaps twenty minutes, and Suzannah didn't know whether he was awake or asleep.

Although how he could sleep at a time like this she couldn't imagine. They were close now, so close she couldn't have slept if her life depended on it. Trent, on the other hand, appeared as calm and relaxed as a man could get.

As if feeling her gaze on him, he rolled onto one side, shoving the hat to the back of his head. "Time to go," he said pleasantly.

She bit her lip and glanced quickly at Jenny, who sat with her back against a huge boulder while she scribbled in a small notebook. "Uh...about this morning, Trent..."

He stood a bit stiffly. "What about it?"

She squinted up at him, looming so tall and unrelenting above her where she sat cross-legged in the grass. "Just that...maybe I do owe you an apology. I had everything under control, but I suppose I can't blame you for not knowing that. I'm no tenderfoot. I wasn't in any real danger."

He heaved an exasperated sigh. "Suzannah, that stud is a wild animal. If he's cornered, he'll do any damned thing that's necessary to hang on to his freedom, including run over *you*."

She thrust out her jaw. "I can take care of myself."

"Famous last words." He gave her a dark glance.

She tried another tack. "Trent, you do realize that in every version of the legend in which the white stallion is captured, he dies before surrendering his freedom."

"That's just a tall tale. Nobody, including a horse, ever died of a broken heart." His laughter was completely unexpected. "You never give up, do you?" He shook his head as if in wonder and turned to retrieve his horse.

AT PRECISELY THREE o'clock, Jenny and Suzannah saddled their horses and rode northeast, as Trent had instructed. They moved steadily but without undue haste, although every nerve of Suzannah's body screamed at her to hurry.

An hour and a half later, they spotted the wild herd grazing on a hillside below, the stolen mare with them. The two women exchanged triumphant glances; this was it.

They separated, Jenny riding to the left and Suzannah to the right. They'd work their way down the hill as unobtrusively as possible, then burst upon the herd and drive the startled animals before them toward Trent, waiting with lariat at the ready.

We couldn't have done this without him, Suzannah freely admitted to herself. Black Jack reached the bottom of the hill and stepped out into a meadow. Trent might be an unyielding block of granite, but he was the kind of man you wanted at your side through any sort of adversity.

The white stallion's shrill trumpeting call sent shivers up her spine. Shifting in her saddle, she saw Pegasus poised on a small hillock to her left, where he could overlook the meadow and his grazing harem. Nervous and alert, he pawed the ground and tossed his head, his long mane streaming out behind him.

Then he leapt down and raced toward his band, neck arched and nostrils flared.

Suzannah nudged Black Jack forward. Where was Jenny? They were supposed to keep the herd moving in the proper direction once the run started. That would take both of them and a whole lot of luck to accomplish.

Normally, anyway. This time, it didn't even take one of them. Pegasus led his mares straight into the trap as if it was preordained. Suzannah and Black Jack followed at a dead run, and her excitement grew with every stride.

As the meadow narrowed toward the rocky passage leading to higher ground, the stallion dropped back. Suzannah saw him nip ruthlessly at the laggards in his band, driving them ahead of him.

Reaching the funnel itself, the animals became a milling mass of horseflesh. Dirt and dust and clods of earth flew from beneath their hooves. The stallion's increased efforts to push them through the bottleneck seemed only to confuse the issue.

Where was Trent? Suzannah tried to slow Black Jack, suddenly aware that she was too close to the fleeing horses. Without Jenny on the left, the entire herd could turn and race away in that direction.

Jenny appeared at that very moment, leaning low over Tramp's neck while her mare galloped flat out to make up the ground they'd lost. The wild mares turning her way pulled back; the one in the lead saw the only escape left and pivoted toward the funnel.

Jenny brought Tramp to a sliding stop beside Suzannah. "Sorry," she shouted. "I got hung up, but it looks like I made it in time."

Suzannah nodded, peering into the confusing mass of horseflesh plunging through the small opening. "No harm done. I think it worked, Jen. *It worked!*"

She kicked her horse into a gallop and rode after the herd through the opening, which was no wider than eight feet. The first thing she saw on the other side was Trent, still astride his horse, working a lariat pulled taut around the neck of Martin's mare.

Elation filled her and she let out a whoop. "You did it!" she shouted, pulling Black Jack up. "You did it, Trent!"

Busy with the mare, he spared her barely a glance. Excited by the chase, Black Jack danced a few steps and she took a moment to settle him down, then brought him back around so she could see Trent subdue Martin Young's bay.

Relief shuddered through her. Up until this very minute, she hadn't been sure which animal Trent would go for first, the mare or the stallion. "You're wonderful!" she shouted to be heard. "I take back everything I said about you—almost!"

He gave her a startled glance. "Dammit, woman, where the hell's that stallion?"

"Gone! They're all gone!" Giddy with happiness, she watched the man reel in the still-struggling mare. Her heart seemed to swell with an emotion with which she'd had very little experience, and her smile threatened to split her face. "It's better this way," she said.

"Better for whom?" He flung the words at her, taking a few extra turns of the rope around the saddle horn.

"For all of us." Surely he could see that. "For you, the stallion—for me and Brittany Daniels and Martin Young and everybody concerned. Pegasus won, Trent. He deserved to win and he did."

With the mare subdued, Trent was finally free to look Suzannah full in the face. "*This* time," he said, his voice lashing at her. "Pegasus won *this* time. I had three ropes, Suzannah. The first one missed the stallion, the second took the mare, and I didn't get a chance to throw the third one. But I will. This isn't over, not by a long shot."

Stunned, she sat there while he led the mare away.

CHAPTER SIX

THE MIGHTY HORSE-HUNTERS straggled into Addison Tuesday noon, led by a tired and cranky Rex Glenn. They found Suzannah, Jenny and Jim Trent waiting at the Lobo Café—with Martin Young's mare tied out front.

"Well I'll be double-damned," Rex Glenn snarled, removing his Stetson to run a hand through his gray hair in frustrated annoyance. "How in the name of thunder did you manage that?"

Suzannah grinned at her father's display of irritation. "Blind stupid luck?" she teased.

"Or outside help." Rex darted a baleful glance at Trent. "Little surprised to see you buttin' in."

"Hell, Rex," Trent drawled, "I just happened to run into them. Couldn't very well let two women wander around out there all alone, now, could I?"

Rex didn't reply, just watched men, women and children "oohing" and "aahing" around the mare. She stood there as docile as if she'd never heard of wild horses, let alone run free with them for a few days.

But as the approval and admiration simmered down, a new and disturbing element arose to take its place. Suzannah realized what was happening when she caught a few inflammatory phrases—like "white bandit" and "danged thief" and "nip this in the bud."

She edged closer.

"...and this likely won't be the last we hear of that wild stallion," Martin predicted to the group of men and boys nodding their complete agreement. "As long as there's a wild hoss roamin' the countryside, we're gonna have to keep our mares locked up. And you know how much fun that is."

"Somebody oughtta do something about that thievin' stallion," a cowboy remarked.

"Somebody oughtta *shoot* him," Rex corrected. He glanced around—guiltily, Suzannah thought—and saw she'd heard. "Well, somebody should," he insisted. "That hoss ain't about to change his ways. We can't afford to let him play fast and loose with our animals, and that's a fact."

"Hold on a minute." Without even raising his voice, Trent dominated the crowd as easily as Suzannah controlled a classroom full of children. "We got the mare back. All's well that ends well, am I right?"

"I suppose, but—"

"No buts." For a moment he scanned the circle of faces as if seeking an ally. And finding none. "We don't want anybody going off half-cocked. There are a lot of sides to this question." He nodded toward Suzannah. "We don't want to alienate all the dyed-in-the-wool animal lovers unnecessarily, now do we."

"What does that mean, *unnecessarily?*" Suzannah, though severely outnumbered, couldn't let it pass. "Jim Trent, you know very well—"

"Hush, Suzy. Let me have my say and then you can have yours," he interrupted her, but gently. He turned to meet Rex Glenn's stern gaze. "Look, I know how you ranchers feel about wild horses. But that's still no reason to consider them nothing more than living targets for shooting practice."

A murmur of halfhearted protest arose. "Now looky here, Trent," Martin Young objected unhappily. "We're not some gun-happy lynch mob."

"Yeah, yeah, none of you would ever do a thing like that." Trent dismissed that argument. "But just in case you're ever tempted, let me remind you that the Free-Roaming Horse and Burro Act of 1971 makes it a crime to kill, injure, harass or capture such animals on public lands."

"But they ain't on public lands," Martin countered to nods of agreement.

"Nope. Last I saw, they were on *my* land," Trent shot back.

"Which just happens to be bordered on two sides by public land and on the third by the Monarch," Rex interjected. "What's your interest in this, anyway, Trent? Looks to me like you're just about the only one who can afford to be generous, seein' as how you don't have any stock to be stole."

"I've got a few head, and I'll have more within the next couple of weeks," Trent said. "But that's got nothing to do with it, Rex. Hell, my solution's the logical one, if you'll all calm down long enough to think straight. Let me handle this my way, and I'll take that stallion out of circulation for good. That's what you ranchers want, and I can do it without bloodshed—which is what Suzannah wants."

"No!" Rex and Suzannah exclaimed in unison.

Suzannah, appalled at finding herself on the same side of an argument as her father, nevertheless rushed ahead. "What would the stallion's life be without his freedom? He's too old to make that adjustment, Trent.''

''You think we'd ever trust havin' that animal around?'' Rex chimed in. ''You might catch him. You might even ride him a time or two or ten. But you'll never tame him.''

Trent looked out at the hostile expressions, his own unreadable. ''Watch me,'' he said.

Rex snorted. ''You're worse than those two gals,'' he said. ''This is nothin' more than that 'romance of the West' bull—''

''Watch it, Pop! There are children present.''

There were, indeed—almost the entire Saturday-morning reading group, including Brittany, Ashley, Jessica and Joshua. They milled around the fringes of the crowd, keenly interested in the goings-on.

Joshua sidled up to Suzannah and gave her a thumbs-up and a wink. ''Don't let 'em push you around, Miss Glenn,'' he advised before scooting off again.

Rex was appealing to Trent. ''Why don't you just stay out of this?'' he asked plaintively. ''If the stallion leading that band is the same one Suzannah saw all those years ago, he can't be any spring chicken. You know as well as I do, once those wild ones get a few years on 'em, they won't learn sic'im.''

A hint of a grin touched Trent's lips. ''We may just be wastin' our breath arguing about this. Last I saw of that wild herd, they were hightailin' it back in the direction they'd come from.''

''That's right,'' Suzannah agreed. ''With any luck, we've seen the last of them.'' She darted a swift glance at Trent, a warning to him to let the argument drop.

He shrugged, and Rex seemed to take that for agreement. Suzannah knew better.

She knew Trent hadn't changed his mind at all. The only reason the stallion wasn't pinned up at the Crazy Ace right this minute was that Trent had missed his first throw of the rope. He was as dedicated to capturing Pegasus as she was to keeping the wild horse free, and as Rex was to seeing him dead.

"Whatever." Martin Young patted Trent on the shoulder. "You and them two gals brought in my mare, so I guess you'll be splittin' the reward."

Trent recoiled. "Not me," he said, as if the entire subject was beneath his dignity. "Give it to them."

"I don't want it," Suzannah said incredulously. "I had nothing to do with catching your mare. I was just there to make sure nothing happened to the stallion."

Jenny was the only one left. "No way," she declined. "I went along for the ride, that's all. Trent did all the work. Give it to him."

Martin chortled, rubbing his hands together with glee. "Looks like I just saved me five hundred bucks," he crowed.

Trent grinned. "Not quite. How about making that check out to the Addison Community Helping Hand Fund? That'll put it to good use."

A murmur of approval swept through the crowd. Suzannah, tired of arguing and tired physically, turned to worm her way toward the door to the Lobo Café. Behind her, she heard a male voice warn, "That's fine this time, but what'll we do if that white outlaw resumes his thieving ways?"

That, in her opinion, was the big question. But after two days spent on the range, she was too worn out to worry about it at the moment—until Ashley ran up and threw her arms around her teacher's waist.

"Oh, thank-you-thank-you-thank-you, Miss Glenn!" the little girl gushed. "I knew you wouldn't let Pegasus down!"

"Not on purpose, Ash," Suzannah said with a sigh. "Not on purpose."

INSIDE THE NEARLY EMPTY café, Miss Louise sat alone in a back booth. "When did you arrive?" Suzannah asked with an exhausted sigh, sliding in to sit opposite the older woman.

Miss Louise stirred her coffee. "During Trent's speech."

"Which one?" Suzannah gestured to Mike to bring another cup of coffee.

"The one about the Free-Roaming Horse and Burro Act. Boy's done his homework about that. Only problem is, somebody decides to take a shot at that stallion or any other wild horse, and a snowball's got a better chance in Hades than the BLM has of getting a conviction."

Growing up a rancher's daughter, Suzannah had no particular love for the Bureau of Land Management. But among other things, it was the BLM's job to protect and manage the wild herds, and in this case she was in perfect sympathy with them.

Miss Louise took a sip of coffee, then placed her cup back on its saucer. Everybody else at the Lobo drank from cheap ceramic mugs; Miss Louise had her own china cup. "So how'd it go out there in the wide open spaces? You girls have fun alone with a handsome cowboy?"

Suzannah made a face. "I wouldn't call it fun." Mike plunked her mug of coffee down on the table, and she thanked him with a quick smile.

When he'd gone, she continued, "Miss Louise, Trent's almost as hardheaded as Pop. You should have seen him out there chasing that herd. He really got into it."

"Men like that sort of thing," Miss Louise said. "They've been chasing and catching wild horses ever since there *were* wild horses, I imagine. Of course, it used to be a lot simpler than it is now."

Suzannah sipped her coffee. "How so?"

"There were so many of them, then—the plains and mountains were black with wild horses. They weren't all plugs, either. But I can't remember a time when the ranchers weren't willing to try just about anything to get rid of them. Range robbers, they called them when I was a girl."

That would have been in the twenties, Suzannah realized with a few mental computations. "Grandpa told me about the time just a hundred years or so ago when a few local cowpunchers decided to trail a herd of wild horses to the Klondike," she said. "Grandpa said they figured they'd not only get rid of a few pests but make a little money in the process."

Miss Louise smiled. "That was a tale well told around here for many years. They started with a big bunch and got something like two or three head through—and it took 'em two years to do it. No money in that. But I remember well the county roundups in the twenties, when thousands of wild horses were shipped out of the country and sold for a few dollars a head."

"Grandpa said that sometimes bounties were put on wild horses—said a lot of them were shot for two dollars a head." Suzannah shivered. "At least now there are a few sanctuaries where they're safe."

"If they'll stay there and not wander away. Men!" Miss Louise shook her head impatiently. "They don't seem constitutionally able to abide any wild thing except themselves. Mustanging was a way of life for every young daredevil in the county when I was growing up. The fewer the horses, the more determined those young bucks were to track 'em down. No wonder wild horses went the way of the buffalo. Why, even your father—" She stopped, casting her companion a guilty glance.

"What?" Suzannah demanded. "You don't mean to tell me my father chased wild horses with anything on his mind but their destruction?"

"I'm rambling," Miss Louise said hastily. "All I care to say on the subject is that I think you are absolutely correct in the position you've taken. There's few enough of those horses left and nothing to be gained by their capture or destruction."

Suzannah's sentiments, exactly. But still, she wondered what Miss Louise had been about to say.

"I TELL YOU, I'd have paid to see Trent lay a loop over that mare's head," Rex said during dinner at the Monarch. "That boy's as good a hand with stock as I've ever seen. It's just pure pleasure to watch him in action. Pass the salt, will you, Suzy?"

Suzannah did, trying to figure out what her father was up to with his enthusiastic ramblings. Why in the world did he keep going on about Jim Trent?

Rex gave her a sly glance. "How'd you say he come to be out there with you girls?"

"I didn't," Suzannah retorted, "but now that you've brought the subject up, it was no accident. I went looking for him. I figured if anybody was going to find those horses, it'd be Trent."

"You got that right." Rex sawed at his steak. "You're not interested in the boy, are you?" he asked abruptly.

Suzannah's fork clattered on her plate. "No!" Had her father changed his mind about Trent's suitability as husband material? If he was reverting to his old matchmaking ways, she'd fight him with every breath in her body. Her father was *not* going to tell her what to do—about anything.

Rex chewed thoughtfully on his steak. He didn't look upset by her vehement denial; in fact, his nod conveyed satisfaction.

He swallowed. "Good!" he boomed. "I like the boy—even admire him in some areas. But I'll be damned if I'd enjoy spendin' the next twenty-five years buttin' heads with him, even if he did get over his rollin'-stone ways and settle down—which I don't for a minute think he's about to do. However—" he gave her a calculating glance "—have you met the new partner John Beeson brought into his law firm? He's from Denver, so there's hope for him, even if he does dress like a tenderfoot."

"No, I haven't met him. I don't *want* to meet him. I've got plenty of time to find a husband. I'm not over the hill yet."

"Oh, no?" He eyed her insolently. "Neither am I, but I see it comin' up fast. What we need here at the Monarch is kids...."

It was a familiar argument and one with which they both felt comfortable. As she said all the usual things, heard all the usual responses, she spared just a quick thought to Jim Trent.

So Rex Glenn didn't enjoy butting heads with the new owner of the Crazy Ace.

Well, well, well...

SUZANNAH SAT in the shade of a tall cottonwood on the lawn behind the library. Saturday had turned out to be so beautiful she hadn't had the heart to keep the children pinned up inside.

They sprawled around her on the grass, most of them in the sunshine, some with eyes closed while they listened to her read from a book of myths. She finished a story about Pegasus and closed the volume.

"So," she said, "what do you think of that?"

Joshua squashed a bug on the grass and sat up. "Awesome!" he said enthusiastically. "I like the part where they cut off the head of that Mud... Mud...

"Medusa," Brittany supplied officiously.

"Yeah," Joshua agreed, "and she had snakes for hair and turned people to stone, she was so ugly. She was the ugliest girl in the world—except for Brittany!"

He ducked just in time to avoid Brittany's sandal, aimed directly at his head.

Suzannah took charge. "Calm down, kids, or I'll have to send you all home early. Jessica, what did you like about the story of Peg—"

She turned her head to smile at the child and her glance met Trent's. He'd come up quietly to stand behind the children, his long lean body draped over the top rail of the wooden fence that defined the library's back lawn. He was smiling.

Suzannah swallowed hard, completely forgetting what she'd been saying.

"That's Peg-asus, Miss Glenn," Brittany supplied, "and what I liked was—"

Suzannah came back to her senses belatedly. "I'm sorry, Brittany. You can be next. It's Jessica's turn now."

"I liked the three Georgians," Jessica said.

"That's Gorgons, honey. What did you like about them?"

Jessica frowned. "I don't know. That there were three of them and they were best friends?" She looked at Ashley and Brittany and grinned.

"Ugly friends!" Joshua shouted. "They were so butt-ugly they turned people to rocks! They—"

Suzannah half rose to quell the boy's enthusiasm, but Trent beat her to it. Leaning over, he plucked Joshua off the grass and planted him on his feet.

Joshua whirled, his eyes opening wide in shocked surprise. Realizing who'd accosted him, his jaw dropped. *"Jim Trent!"* he breathed.

"Son," Trent said gently, "I think you owe these ladies an apology."

"I—I do?" Joshua frowned, looking thoroughly confused. "Why?"

"Because gentlemen don't speak to ladies that way." Trent cocked his head, regarding the boy quizzically. "Is your father Cub Hickman?" he asked suddenly.

Joshua, still looking dazed, managed a nod. "How'd you know?" he burst out.

Trent grinned. "Because I went to school with him and you look just like he did then." He bent his long legs to bring himself down to the boy's level. "Listen to me and listen good. I know your father and I know if he thought you were pickin' fights with girls, he'd have your hide stretched out on the side of the barn before sundown."

Joshua gulped. "You won't tell him?" he pleaded.

"Nah, we'll keep it between us—unless it happens again. Then I'll have to take action."

Trent stood up and took a step toward Suzannah, who had listened with a slight smile on her face. Joshua reached out and caught Trent by a belt loop.

The man looked at the boy questioningly. "Something else before I carry your teacher off and buy her some lunch at the Lobo?"

Joshua licked his lips. "Uh...could I have your autograph? Please? I saw you ride two years ago at Cheyenne Days, and you gotta be the best bronc buster in Wyoming—maybe the world! I wanna be just like you when I grow up. Please, can I have your autograph?"

"Please?" echoed the other children, jumping to their feet and clustering around the tall man.

"I'll get paper and a pencil," Suzannah offered, "but that's all. Nobody's carrying me off *anywhere!*"

SUZANNAH MET Trent's amused gaze across the scarred wooden table at the Lobo.

"So nobody was gonna carry you off anywhere," he teased.

She lifted her shoulders in an airy gesture. "It took you so long to sign those autographs that I got hungry," she said. "Besides, I needed to explain something to you."

"Such as?" He put his straw aside and picked up the glass of iced tea.

"In some circles it's an insult these days to call females 'ladies,'" she said. "Don't you want to be politically correct?"

He frowned as if considering. Then he grinned. "Nope. Don't think I could, even if I tried. There's something wrong with a society that downgrades ladies."

She shook her head in amazement. "Jim Trent, you sound just like—" Her eyes flew wide. Heaven help her; she was having lunch with a man who sounded just like her father. "—a man looking for trouble," she concluded lamely and mendaciously.

"Then why did you accept my gracious invite?"

"I told you. I was hungry and saw no reason to pass up a free lunch..." *Just because I get tongue-tied every time you smile at me,* she added privately. She put all her attention into peeling the paper off her straw and sticking it into her glass.

Mike served their chicken-fried-steak sandwiches. "Not a very politically correct choice," Trent pointed out. "Thought you'd be into nuts and grains and berries, being so politically correct yourself."

She made a face and turned to her favorite lunch, the one she never allowed herself to order when she ate with her father. It was too much fun to hear his howls of outrage when she stuck with "rabbit food."

They ate for a few moments and then Trent said into the surprisingly comfortable silence, "I've done a lot of work on the Crazy Ace, but I've still got a lot more to do, especially in the house—curtains and such. I'd be pleased to have you drop by one day soon and give me a little guidance."

She was touched that he'd ask. "Sure. Maybe I will." She shifted the sandwich around between restless fingers. "And you drop by the Monarch, too."

Trent raised his dark brows. "Think Rex'd go for that?"

Suzannah lifted her chin defensively. "The day I can't invite anyone I want to the ranch is the day I move out for good," she declared. "Besides, he likes you. He just doesn't—" She bit her lip, unwilling to tell him that he was probably the only unmarried man between the age of twenty and forty that Rex wasn't touting as potential husband material.

"Yeah, what he doesn't like are people arguing with him." Trent didn't look as if that bothered him any. "Hey, I'm back to stay, so he better get used to it."

Back to stay. Suzannah smiled and took a bite of her sandwich. "Then we're really going to be neighbors." She wiped greasy fingers on her paper napkin. "I guess as long as we don't have wild horses to argue about, that shouldn't prove to be a problem."

He nodded, his grin coming slow and sexy. "That's the way I figure it," he agreed.

"Any sign of the herd on your land since you caught the mare?"

"None. I'm beginning to think they're gone for good."

"You look as if you have mixed feelings about that," she said. "I'd expect you to be disappointed."

"I am. I want that stallion—for a lot of reasons. But on the other hand—" he gave her a smile so brilliant it left her weak "—if the herd was still tearing up the countryside, I doubt we'd be sitting here like this."

He had a good point. She was just about to say so when Mike galloped up.

"Food all right?" he inquired.

"Great," Trent said. "Nobody puts out a chicken-fried steak like the Lobo."

The boy nodded and started to leave, then turned back. "By the way," he said, "you guys hear about what happened to Mae Pettigrew's garden?"

WHAT HAPPENED to Mae Pettigrew's garden was enough to spoil lunch, the day and possibly all hopes for peaceful coexistence in Addison County, Wyoming. For what had happened could be summed up quite simply: the wild herd was back.

Back and running roughshod over local agricultural enterprises, although Mike reported that Mae herself was philosophical. "Not much use offerin' a reward for a tomato-killer," she'd remarked.

There'd been renewed griping about the wild herd, Mike said, but it hadn't precipitated another crisis.

Yet.

"Well, hell," Trent said after the bearer of bad news departed. Although he still yearned to get his hands on the stallion, he also yearned to get his hands on Suzannah. He hadn't yet figured out a way he could do both.

Across the table, Suzannah groaned. He recognized the worry in her brown eyes and wanted to offer reassurance, but didn't; anything he said would be a lie. If the stallion was back, Trent would be hot on his trail at the first opportunity.

Her smile looked sad. "And we were getting on so well," she said.

"That doesn't have to change." Her right hand lay on the table beside her plate, and he put his own hand over it, just to see how she'd react. Her fingers stiffened beneath his, and he waited for her to relax; she didn't.

"It already has," she said regretfully. She slid her hand from beneath his and stood up. "It would be hypocritical to pretend otherwise unless... Have you changed your mind about catching Pegasus?"

"No," he said with complete, though damning, honesty.

"Then I guess that's that."

"That's *not* that. My invitation to visit the Ace stands."

"Thanks, but I... I'm going to be pretty busy the rest of the summer." Almost as an afterthought, she added, "And thanks for the lunch. Perhaps I'll see you around."

With an exclamation of disgust, he leaned back in his seat. "Dammit, Suzy, this wild-horse business doesn't have to mess everything up for us. Be reasonable."

She straightened her shoulders and looked down her nose at him. "Nothing personal, Trent, but *you're* the one who's not being reasonable—and that's only one of many areas in which we disagree. If I want to fight about those horses, I don't have to go to strangers. I can always stay home and fight with my father."

"Okay—but the invitation stands. If you come to your senses, you know where to find me."

She shrugged as if it didn't matter and turned away. He watched her walk out of the Lobo, admiring her poise almost as much as he admired the rounded curves of her backside.

Too bad she had to take that attitude, but he wasn't changing his plans to accommodate a woman, any woman, not even one who appealed to him as mightily as did Rex Glenn's fiery daughter.

Not that he'd given up on her, though, not by a long shot. He dropped bills and coins onto the table and headed for the door. She'd wise up. One of these days he'd look up from some chore at the Crazy Ace and see a Monarch pickup bouncing down the dirt road toward him.

The day that happened he'd know he'd won the battle of nerves.

"What're you so happy about all of a sudden?" Mike wanted to know as Trent strode past on his way to the door.

Trent didn't answer, just grinned, waved and kept going.

CHAPTER SEVEN

ROD DROPPED BY the Monarch a week later. "If you came to see Pop, he's not here," Suzannah said in greeting. Actually, she was delighted to see Rod, figuring he might know how Trent was doing. She hadn't seen him for a full week—seven days—since they'd heard about Mae Pettigrew's garden. "I just got here myself from my Saturday-morning reading class," she added.

Rod leaned down to pat Shep, one of the Monarch's many sheepdogs. "I came to see you, I guess."

She laughed. "You guess? Aren't you sure?"

"Uh, Suzannah..."

"Rod, old buddy, you look like a man with a problem." She slipped her arm through his and led him toward the house. "Come inside and I'll fix us both a glass of lemonade. We can drink it on the terrace out back and talk about anything your little ol' heart desires."

ROD FOUND IT HARD to say his piece. Always a glib talker, now he seemed more interested in staring at the far horizon than in kidding around the way he usually did.

After a few abortive attempts at small talk, Suzannah sat back to sip her drink and wait for him to tell her what was bothering him, which he'd do in his own good time.

At least ten minutes later, he sighed and slumped lower in his padded lawn chair. "Damn!" he burst out. "I'll bet you wonder what my problem is."

"Well, yes, but I figure you'll talk when you're ready."

"Okay, I'm ready." He drew a deep breath. "It's the Rocking L. I just found out something..." He shook his head and shuddered.

Suzannah frowned. She'd fully expected his problems were romantic. "Problems at the ranch?"

"Big problems. Turns out Trent's been... Hell, I guess the proper word for it is 'subsidizing.' He's been subsidizing the ranch for years. The worst is past, apparently. Pop said last year we actually broke even, and he expects a profit from now on."

"That's a relief," Suzannah murmured automatically, but she was thinking, *Trent's been supporting his uncle's ranch? No one's even suspected.*

Rod sighed. "This really throws me for a loop. I always thought of Trent as sort of a... Well, hell, I may as well be blunt and say it right out. He was always the poor relation, growing up. And now I find out the poor relation has been keeping the old family homestead afloat for years."

Bracing his forearms on his spread thighs, Rod clasped his hands and leaned forward, his expression pensive. "Don't get me wrong—I like my cousin a lot. But he's always been so damned *good* at everything. I guess I was willing to take any edge I could get."

"Like being the son and heir," Suzannah suggested softly. *Poor Trent.*

"Yeah, like that. Hell, he was fifteen and I was thirteen when his folks died and he moved up here from Texas. All of a sudden I had somebody right under my nose who was a better cowboy, a better student, more popular." He gave her an unhappy glance.

"Two years makes a lot of difference when you're kids," she pointed out.

"Nice try." His expression remained bleak. "We got older, but it's the same today with me twenty-nine and him thirty-one."

"Does Trent know how you feel?"

"Hell, no!" He looked shocked at the idea. "Anyway, now that he's settled down on the Crazy Ace and fixin' to stock it, I feel a little funny findin' out what he did for us. It's like I owe him something all of a sudden."

"Instead of the other way around," she murmured.

"Huh?"

"Rod, I'm sure he must have felt he owed *you* something, you and your folks. You took him in, took care of him."

"Well, sure. He's family."

"That's right. And you're his. So—"

"That damned stallion!"

Rex Glenn's furious roar brought both Rod and Suzannah bolting to their feet. They turned toward the back door in unison just as the tall rancher burst through.

Suzannah started toward her father. "What is it? What's happened?"

Rex slammed his Stetson down on the flagstones and stomped it, for all the world like a raging bull. "That damned wild stallion has made off with two of my mares! Registered stuff—grabbed 'em outta the north pasture before I could move 'em in closer.''

Her heart sank. Ever since the Mae Pettigrew garden incident, she'd been waiting and hoping. Apparently her hopes had come to naught.

Rex quit stomping to glare at the hat smashed all out of shape beneath his feet. Still swearing, he snatched it up and glowered at his daughter.

''Well, that tears it,'' he announced in a voice filled with utter finality. ''I'm offering a reward for that stud, a reward so big it'll bring out every man and boy in Addison County.''

''Dead or alive?'' Suzannah hurled back at him.

''Whatever it takes!''

Slapping the hat on his head, Rex roared into the house, yelling for Shorty Williams, his foreman. Suzannah turned to Rod in an agony of dread. ''Here we go again. How on earth am I going to stop him?''

Rod shook his head. ''Damned if I know, Suzannah. He sure sounds serious this time.''

''Well, I'm serious, too! This has gotten personal. I have to find some way to protect those horses.''

''You could report him to the BLM.''

''He's still my father!'' She couldn't believe Rod would suggest such a thing. ''Weren't we just talking about blood being thicker than water? Pop would never forgive me if I did that, and I wouldn't blame him.''

''I didn't mean you *should*. It was just an option.'' Rod put an arm around her shoulder. ''Suzannah, when you're between a rock and a hard place, you might as well pick the hard place.''

She darted him a dubious glance. ''And that means . . . ?''

"Your old man hates wild horses in every way, shape and form—he's the rock. Trent's the hard place—he never met a horse he didn't like, so he means the wild herd no harm. He just wants to play cowboy."

She saw his point. "So you're suggesting . . . ?"

He nodded. "Honey, if there was any way I could help you, you know I would. But I've got to live here and I'm no hero, so there's no way I'm going up against your pa. Trent, on the other hand... Well, my cousin's a man who likes a good fight."

Suzannah groaned. "But I've already tried to bring him around to my way of thinking and got nowhere with him."

Rod shrugged. "Then I suggest you try harder."

SUZANNAH HAD BEEN to the Crazy Ace Ranch—officially—only a few times, and not at all in the past several years. Nevertheless, the minute Rod left she climbed into one of the Monarch's pickups and headed for Trent's new place. If she waited, she might chicken out and change her mind.

The sad truth was she needed help, and Rod was right when he'd said the only person who could and might give it to her was Jim Trent.

But she wouldn't play games, she promised herself. She'd lay her cards on the table. "Trent," she'd say, very calm and businesslike, "I have no reason to think I can change your mind, but I'm going to try, anyway. Help me get that wild herd out of the county before my father or some other trigger-happy rancher shoots first and asks questions later."

And Trent would reply, "Why should I, Suzannah?"

And she'd say, "This is more important to me than it is to you. Do it for the heck of it. Do it for old time's sake. Do it because I'm desperate. I won't question your motivation if you'll just do it."

Then if he still refused, she'd beg.

She actually rehearsed, saying the words aloud as the pickup bounced over the rutted dirt road. The closer she got to the Crazy Ace, the more nervous she became.

She had never dreamed she'd ever be reduced to this: begging a favor from a man. It was a humbling experience, to be sure. She could only hope she'd be a better woman for it, since her motives were unselfish.

The pickup bounced beneath the weathered old sign over the entrance to the ranch yard that proclaimed this to be the Crazy Ace, then jolted to a stop before the door. Waiting for the dust to settle, she gripped the steering wheel until her knuckles turned white.

She couldn't do this. It was too humiliating.

She had to do this. Too much was riding on it to turn tail and run.

"Are you going to sit there all day, or do you plan to get out?"

At the sound of Trent's voice almost in her ear, Suzannah started and whipped around on the bench seat, her heart hammering. He stood there grinning at her, as if they'd never had a cross word in their lives.

"I—I'm getting out." She fumbled for the door, trying to remember the lines she'd rehearsed so diligently. "Trent," she began haltingly, "I know I have no right—"

"Sure you do, honey." He opened the door and reached for her hand to help her down from the high seat.

The moment his warm brown fingers closed around her cold quaking ones, she was lost. Sliding out of the truck, she struggled to remember what it was she needed to say. "I must be businesslike and calm," she reminded herself.

"With me? No chance."

To her horror, she realized she'd spoken aloud what should have been mental reminders. Before she could recover from that shock, he'd gathered her into his arms.

"What are you doing?" She pushed weakly against his muscular arms. Which wasn't easy, since it felt so right to be standing here in his embrace.

He put her from him, still grinning. "I'm pleased you decided to accept my invitation. After the way you walked out on me at the Lobo the other day, well, let's say I'm pleased and surprised."

"Oh, well, about that—"

He went right on talking. "Gets lonesome out here in the country. If I had more company, maybe I wouldn't get so carried away."

"Maybe." She swallowed hard. To give herself time to gather her wits, she smoothed her hair off her face. Now, what had she intended to say? Oh, yes. "I imagine you wonder why I'm here," she began in a squeaky voice.

He smiled again—she wished he'd stop that—and his blue eyes literally sparkled. "I know why you're here," he said.

A tide of relief washed over her. "You do?"

"Sure." He hooked his thumbs in his belt loops and rocked back on his heels. "I conjured you up."

"You conjured...?" She frowned, completely confused. She couldn't follow what he was saying and concentrate on her own lines at the same time: *Ask a favor... wild herd... I'll beg if I have to....*

If he noticed anything amiss, he didn't let on. "I was working out back with the horses, and all of a sudden I thought, what I need right now is some company," he drawled. "And then I thought, who would I like to see driving up that road this very minute?"

She stared at him, mesmerized. "Me?" she whispered.

He nodded. "You. It's right neighborly of you to come callin', Miss Suzannah. You didn't happen to bring a plate of brownies or chocolate-chip cookies to welcome me to the neighborhood, did you?"

"Oh!" She felt awful; of course, she should have brought a housewarming gift. It hadn't even occurred to her.

Trent slipped an arm around her shoulders. "Never mind," he comforted her. "That oversight will give you an excuse to come back."

He squeezed her shoulders lightly and she shivered despite the warmth of the day. Pulling herself together, she launched into her prepared speech again. "Okay, well, the reason I've presumed to come here is—"

"My nearest neighbor doesn't need a reason to come calling, other than the obvious."

"Th-the obvious?" She wished he'd remove his arm from her shoulders but dreaded the moment he would.

"Sure. I invited you and you're curious to see what I'm doin' with the old place. And I'm sure you wanted to know if I need any help."

"Do you?" she couldn't stop herself from asking.

"As a matter of fact," he said, "I do. I've got a pretty good handle on the outside, but I haven't any idea what I should do about the house. What I need is a woman's point of view."

"That's doubtless true, but interior decoration's not exactly my strong suit. I'm a lot more comfortable branding a cow than I am threading a sewing machine. All I want is a chance to— What is it?"

He was grinning and shaking his head. "I'm not letting you see the horses until you give me your expert opinion about the house," he teased. "I don't blame you if you're impatient, though. I've got two of the best-looking Appaloosas back there you'll ever see, along with some real nice yearlings, quarter-horse stock."

Throwing up her hands, she surrendered. "Okay, you win!" she exclaimed. "I'm all yours."

The look he gave her in response sent a tremor of excitement through her.

TRENT COULD TELL the house surprised her. Although small, it was cozy and well constructed, with open-beam ceilings and fireplaces in almost every room. She kept touching things, looking up at him with those big brown eyes full of approval.

"Did you bring all this furniture with you?" she asked, clearly amazed.

"I wish I could say yes, since you look so impressed." He patted the back of the big overstuffed living-room couch, positioned to take advantage of a massive stone fireplace. "Gotta tell the truth, though. It came with the place. After Ace died, I guess somebody just covered everything with sheets and walked away."

"The furniture really fits the house." She turned in a circle to admire the total room. "It's all so rustic and . . . and cozy."

"Ace made a lot of it himself. Like the chairs."

He led her into the small dining area at one end of the L-shaped room. Picking up a wooden chair, he showed her how it had been notched, then lashed together with leather thongs.

"It gave the old guy something to do on long cold nights," he said, replacing the chair. "Living out here all alone can be lonely as hell."

She nodded as if she understood. Walking to the stairs, she caressed the log railing as if marveling at its smoothness. "The Crazy Ace is pretty darn isolated. Do you really intend to stay here, or will you get bored and go back to rodeo?" she asked suddenly.

"I always wanted a place of my own," he countered, carefully keeping his tone bland and noncommittal.

"I can understand that, but after what Rod said . . ."

He felt his hackles rise. "What *did* Rod say?"

Her cheeks flushed a becoming shade of rose. "I'm sorry, I shouldn't have mentioned that. He said you'd been more or less supporting the Lowell ranch for a number of years. That means you've got a financial, as well as familial, interest there."

"Not really. It'll be Rod's someday, and that's only right. I want my own place and now I've got it."

She nodded. "Yes, I see that." She licked her lips. "Everybody always knew you *liked* rodeo, but it must be lucrative for you to be able to help your family that way." She plunged on bravely, as if she figured she'd gone too far to back out now. "I'm just trying—not very gracefully—to say I think it was very good of you to help them out, Trent.''

''I gave my family a few bucks when they needed it—big deal.'' He scowled to cover his embarrassment. ''I could support them for the rest of my life and I still wouldn't consider the debt I owe my aunt and uncle paid in full.'' He turned away, feeling uncomfortable. ''Come along and I'll show you the rest of the place.''

He led her through a small tidy kitchen with appliances so old they might be antiques, and through one small and one large bedroom upstairs. She exclaimed over the hand-quilted coverings of both beds but didn't linger to examine them.

He stifled a smile. She took great care to stay beyond his reach, and it wasn't because she found his touch repulsive. Miss Suzannah Glenn was every bit as aware of him as he was of her. That was why she'd come—not to be neighborly, not out of curiosity, not to renew their quarrel over the wild herd.

She was here for the same reason he'd been about to drive over to the Monarch when she'd arrived and saved him a trip. This was better, anyway.

More privacy.

Completing the tour of the house, he led her behind the barn to the corrals. He was proud of the few horses he'd brought in so far and pleased with her enthusiastic appreciation.

''But where's the cattle?'' she asked, glancing around. ''Rod said—''

''Sounds like you've been pumping Rod for information pretty doggoned strong,'' he observed.

She looked embarrassed but undaunted. "Not at all," she said airily. "It's just that he mentioned you were restocking."

"I am, with horses. This is going to be a horse ranch, Suzannah. I'm going to raise and train the best damned horses in the West. Come on into the barn and take a look at the little Appaloosa mare who's going to get me started."

He led her through the open double doors. The mare, tethered in a large stall and ankle-deep in fresh straw, looked up.

"She's gorgeous!" Without hesitation, Suzannah slipped in beside the mare, running her hands over the animal's back, checking her out.

When she returned to stand before him, her face was shining. "I'm impressed," she said. "I really am impressed."

"So am I," Trent said roughly, "with you."

Fed up with waiting, he reached out to slide his hands around her neck, burying his fingers in her thick fall of hair. With his thumbs beneath her jaw, he tilted her head and looked into her face.

And smiled.

TRENT HAD HER NUMBER, no doubt about it. Without hesitation, she slipped her arms around his waist and closed her eyes, waiting for his kiss.

She wasn't disappointed. He kissed her more thoroughly than she'd ever been kissed in her life. And then he kissed her eyes, her cheeks, her throat...

Without surrendering the kiss, he walked her backward until her heel struck something in the straw and she gave a cry. But she was in no danger—of falling, anyway. He lowered her gently until she lay upon a cushion of clean straw. Dimly she realized they must be inside an empty stall, but she didn't open her eyes to find out because she didn't really care.

All she cared about was Trent and the way he made her feel. She couldn't get close enough to him, even when his long lean body half covered hers; she couldn't get enough of his kisses, even when he showered them across her cheek, her throat, down to the V of her cotton blouse.

Had the moment of truth come and gone? Had she been swept willingly past the point of no return? He tugged at the top button of her shirt, and she couldn't find it anywhere in her heart or her mind to resist—until she heard the roar of a vehicle driving into the ranch yard.

Trent froze and lifted his head, his expression first alert and questioning, then angry and frustrated.

"Damn!" He sprang to his feet, leaning over to grab her hand and pull her up, too. "Somebody's here."

"I...who...what?" Still awash in sensual feelings, Suzannah shook her head, trying to clear it, at the same time brushing straw from her jeans.

Trent fastened the two buttons he'd opened on her shirt, his expression rueful. His fingers lingered over their task, the intimate contact with the upper swell of her breast making her tremble. "I'll kill that SOB," he promised, his tone only half-joking. "He deserves to die."

Suzannah could not have agreed more.

Throwing an arm over her shoulders, Trent walked her through the barn and across the yard toward a pickup truck just pulling to a stop. Rod sat behind the wheel, and when he saw them, he grinned.

Seeing who it was, Suzannah felt a jolt of panic. Surely Rod wouldn't say anything about the advice he'd given her that had led her here—but what if he did? Trent would assume that was why she'd let him make love to her.

When, in fact, nothing could have been further from the truth. She'd been unable to help herself. If there'd been an ounce of character or principle in her entire body, she'd never have let him lay a hand on her—at least until he knew why she'd really come to the Crazy Ace.

Now it was too late. He'd put two and two together and come to the inevitable conclusion that she'd been leading him on because she wanted something from him—wanted it desperately enough to go to any extremes to get it.

While she cast about frantically, trying to think of some way to keep Rod from putting his foot in her mouth, Rod leaned out of the cab of the truck. Grinning broadly, he gave them the once-over.

"So. She talked you into it, did she? That's a relief! Now that you've agreed to help her protect that wild herd, Trent, maybe the two of you can finally quit fighting about those damned wild horses."

TRENT WAITED until Suzannah had driven her pickup over a ridge and out of sight before turning on his cousin. Rod took a couple of steps backward, bumping into the rear fender of his truck. He scooted around that barrier.

"Hey, take it easy," Rod pleaded. "How was I to know?"

"Know what?"

"That she'd—that you'd—that both of you—" Rod swallowed hard. "Ah, hell, so she came over here to talk you into helping her—"

"Talk didn't enter into it. She tried *other methods* of convincing me."

Rod shook his head. "Suzannah's not like that. Did you give her a chance?"

"I gave her a lot of chances," Trent snarled. But had he? She'd seemed flustered when she first arrived, and thrown off stride by his teasing. Then their long-simmering mutual attraction had come to a boil— No, dammit, she'd had plenty of opportunity.

Disgusted for doubting himself, Trent turned toward the house but stopped after a few steps. "Wait a minute—the wild band's been seen since Mae Pettigrew's garden got stomped?"

"And how. That stallion made off with a couple of Rex's mares. He's fit to be tied."

"And Suzannah, seeing the handwriting on the wall, came over here to con me into helping her."

Rod looked uncomfortable. "I don't think 'con' is the word I'd use."

"I don't think I give a hoot in hell what word you'd use." Trent lifted his hat and shoved back his hair with his palm before slamming the hat down again. "Get out of here, Rod. I'm in no mood to be hospitable."

"Yeah, sure." Rod edged toward the pickup door. "Couldn't stay, anyway. Jenny's expecting me."

"Why don't you marry that woman and let her keep you out of trouble?" Trent, still dangerously angry, glared at his cousin.

Rod slid behind the wheel and closed the door. "Look who's talking," he jeered. He started the engine before leaning out the window. "But just for the record, that's exactly what I'm planning to do—if she'll have me.''

ANYTHING SHE MIGHT have said would only have made matters worse, so Suzannah hadn't said anything at all. Driving away from the Crazy Ace, she tried to convince herself she'd done the only thing she could.

But had she? She'd not only lost all hope of saving Pegasus and the wild herd, she'd also lost any chance she might have had for a cordial relationship with Jim Trent. Cordial? Remembering the sweetness of his kisses, she groaned out loud.

No way was she indifferent to him, and she couldn't fool herself any longer into pretending she was. On impulse, she turned toward Addison, instead of the Monarch. She needed someone to talk to, someone who might understand. What she didn't need was more of her father's ranting and raving about the theft of the two mares.

Damn, she hadn't even told Trent about that. She'd been so swept up in the pleasure of his company that every rational thought had flown right out of her head, along with her reason for being there. She'd really messed things up this time.

Miss Louise welcomed Suzannah without comment, seating her in the garden at a lacy cast-iron table complete with white linen, fine silver and china. Suzannah nibbled at small cakes, sipped lemonade and wallowed in misery.

Miss Louise picked up her napkin, shaking it out before allowing it to float onto her lap. "Good gracious, girl, you're staring at my snapdragons as if you expect them to attack at any moment. What's troubling you?''

"It's Trent."

With precise care, Miss Louise replaced her silver dessert fork beside her plate. "Dear heart," she said, "has it not yet occurred to you that you've thought and spoken of little else since that man returned to Addison? Except for those wild horses, of course, but everyone's been in a tizzy about them."

"Actually," Suzannah said, "that's been brought home to me rather forcefully." She bit her lip. "Miss Louise, have you ever been in love?''

The silver-haired woman looked taken aback but didn't try to avoid the question. "As a matter of fact, I have. It ended . . . badly."

"I'm sorry." Suzannah knew she shouldn't pursue the subject, but curiosity got the best of her. "What happened?''

"There were . . . problems. He did something my father couldn't forgive. Then, after my father's death, well, it was too late."

"That's so sad." Suzannah felt heartsick and near tears, although she rarely cried. "Why was it too late? Did he die?''

Miss Louise lifted her chin and looked down her nose. "No, you silly child, he didn't die. He married someone else and had you."

Suzannah nearly fell off her chair with astonishment. Rex Glenn, the man of Miss Louise's dreams? "You and *Daddy?* What happened?" she gasped.

"Never mind what happened. It was a long time ago." Miss Louise took Suzannah's hands in both of hers and held them tight. "Perhaps I shouldn't have said anything after keeping the secret all these years, but I...I'm worried about you, dear. Listen to me. Love is where you find it, and it doesn't always knock twice.''

"It's opportunity that doesn't always knock twice," Suzannah said lightly, but she got the point. Not that she was in love with Jim Trent, of course, nor he with her. "What was it Pop did that was so bad your father couldn't forgive him?"

"There is absolutely no need to go into that," Miss Louise said firmly. "Here, have another apricot petit four and tell me what you're going to do about this horse business."

Suzannah accepted the dainty morsel. "I don't really know," she admitted. Looking up suddenly, she added, "Will you help me, Miss Louise? If anyone can handle my father, it's you. Please?"

Miss Louise's aristocratic nostrils flared. "Let me think about this," she said finally. "Just let me think."

CHAPTER EIGHT

"POP, YOU CAN'T DO THIS!"

Rex Glenn paused, his hand on the knob of the kitchen door, to turn an implacable face toward his daughter. "A man's got to do what he thinks is right, Suzannah. Ridding this county of that thieving outlaw horse is something that needs doing. I'm sorry you can't see the situation clearly but—"

"You mean see it your way," she cut in unhappily.

He shrugged. "Same thing. You got a blind spot where those wild horses are concerned."

She gripped the back of a kitchen chair with all her strength. "*Who's* got a blind spot."

His expression turned sorrowful. "Honey, nobody's got any problem with this except you and Trent—and the two of you can't even agree with each other."

That was, alas, too true. She'd never felt more alone and outnumbered.

Torchlight flickered through the kitchen windows as the hunters gathered before first light, preparing for the start of the biggest horse-hunt in modern Wyoming history. Suzannah shuddered. They intended to hunt down Pegasus and his band of mares like vicious predators.

The situation had taken on a particularly serious tone because the stakes were so high: five hundred dollars each for the Monarch mares but five thousand dollars for the stallion—dead or alive, although that was not said openly.

Trent had exploded when he'd heard of it a couple of days before, and he'd tracked Rex down at Stanley's Feed Store to raise hell. Without a word to Jenny or Suzannah, who'd stood watching and listening with mouths agape, Trent had torn into the rancher with a vengeance.

"That's not a reward you're offering on that stallion—it's a bounty," Trent had accused. "You're getting everybody in this part of the state all whipped up about finding that herd. If we're not lucky, somebody's gonna get hurt." His lip curled. "Hell, I'll go get your mares for you if that's what you really want. Just call off your dogs."

Rex had shaken his head with slow finality. "Too late, Trent. If you want to come along to see no one goes off the deep end, we'd be pleased to have you, but—"

"When hell freezes over!" Trent had stomped toward the door, then turned back. "You're creating a mob mentality, and there's no way of knowing where it'll lead. I wouldn't touch this with a ten-foot pole."

When he'd gone, Rex sighed. "Too bad," he said. "Damn, I like that boy! Kinda reminds me of me. But you—" He'd fixed his daughter with a stern gaze. "Stay away from him!"

Now she watched her father walk through the kitchen doorway to join what—if the object of the search was a human being—could only be called vigilantes. She shivered, struck by the primitive vitality of the scene. All these people, lined up against one small, nearly defenseless band of wild horses. It just wasn't fair!

She didn't realize how unfair until Rex called everybody together for last-minute instructions. With a minimum of fuss, the searchers divided into teams to scour the countryside on horseback. Rex, the man who'd started the whole thing, would go up in the recently repaired ranch plane to scout around from the sky.

"But it's illegal to herd wild horses from the air," Suzannah objected.

Martin Young patted her on the shoulder. "Honey, we ain't *tryin'* to herd 'em," he said.

Horrified, she could do nothing but watch as her father and Shorty Williams drove away toward the small ranch airfield while the others mounted up and rode out. Rod saw her standing there alone and guided his horse to her side, a plaintive expression on his face.

"I'm real sorry about this, Suzannah." He fiddled with the reins. "I'll do what I can to protect them if we catch up with the herd."

"Thanks, Rod." She said it knowing that his chances of being able to affect the outcome were slim and none.

But at least he was willing to try, which was more than she could say for anyone else. She watched him ride off, her whole body numb with defeat. There had to be a way—

"Don't let them see you cry."

At the harsh command, she stiffened, then dashed away the dampness on her cheeks. A hand touched her elbow lightly, bringing her to full attention. "Trent," she said without turning. "What are you doing here?"

"I had to see it to believe it."

"Okay, you've seen it."

At that moment, a long black automobile pulled into the ranch yard. Miss Louise had come—too late. She threw open the rear door and stepped out. Winnie, looking sleepy and cross in the driver's seat, slumped back and closed her eyes, prepared to catch forty winks.

"Good morning, Suzannah, Trent." Miss Louise glanced around, pursing her lips. "I see I'm too late."

Suzannah nodded, still fighting tears. "Don't feel too bad," she managed. "I don't suppose there was anything you could have done. I must have said it all—six or seven times, in fact."

"Not everything, my dear." Miss Louise squared her slender shoulders. "I am about to tell you the reason your father despises wild horses. I've kept his secret for many years, and I wouldn't betray him now, but he is acting out of selfish motives."

Fear dried Suzannah's mouth and made her breathing light and shallow. She glanced at Trent, who stared at Miss Louise with a frown on his face.

Miss Louise gestured toward the house. "Let's go inside," she suggested. "This may take a while."

Actually, the bare bones of the story were quite simple.

Miss Louise explained that a good fifty years ago when Rex was a wild young fool, he'd spent much of his free time chasing mustangs—for adventure more than for the small profit that could be had. Once he talked Miss Louise's younger brother, Elwood, into going with him.

"They returned the following day," Miss Louise said, "Rex leading my brother's horse with Elwood's body facedown across the saddle. He'd been trampled by the leader of the wild band.

"Rex was in a very bad way about this, riddled with guilt as you might imagine. My mother, knowing the depth of his remorse, forgave him on the spot, as did I. But my father couldn't bring himself..."

Her voice trailed off and for a moment she stared into space, biting on her pale lower lip. Suzannah sat very still, feeling the long-ago grief of the tragedy. She hadn't even known Miss Louise once had a brother.

Trent, too, seemed moved by the story. He looked at the old woman with something like tenderness in his expression.

Miss Louise cleared her throat and continued more briskly, "My father sent your father away, Suzannah. I lost both my brother and the man I loved that day. Had I been stronger... But I could not imagine defying my father, especially when he was grieving so for my brother. I thought he would get over it in time."

Her silver head sagged. "He didn't, and neither did Rex. Even after my father's death..." She sighed. "And then, of course, Rex married your mother."

After a moment, she managed a tremulous smile. "And that is why your father hates wild horses. Although he is wrong to, at least there is a reason. I intended to confront him with that reason this morning in an attempt to stop him. As usual, I made up my mind too late."

Suzannah stood and put her arms around Miss Louise. "I'm sorry," she whispered. "I knew there had to be something...."

She comforted the woman for a few moments, then glanced around. "Where's Trent?"

"I-isn't he here?" Miss Louise sounded very near to tears.

"No!" Suzannah hurried to the door and looked out.

Jim Trent had unloaded his horse from the trailer behind his pickup truck and was saddling up.

"I'M GOING WITH YOU!" Suzannah shouted, running across the hard-packed earth of the yard. "Wait for me!"

Trent swung into the saddle. "Not a chance. You'd only be in the way."

"I wouldn't! I could help. Trent..." She grabbed at the saddle strings, her hands scraping across the stiff leather of his chaps. The mustang danced sideways and she somehow managed to hang on. "I want to help! I'd rather see them in a corral than buzzard bait!"

"Let go, Suzannah. I'm riding alone."

She clung tighter, her feet barely skimming the ground as the mustang headed out of the yard. "If anyone can find that wild herd, it's you. I made a promise to those kids and I intend to keep it, or as much of it as I can. I'm going!"

Her hands slipped. She clawed at his leg, at the saddle, at the horse...

He left her in the dust. She stared after horse and rider, breathing hard. Damn him! He didn't even look back.

She cupped her mouth with her hands and shouted, "Don't think this settles anything! I'll be right behind you!"

Spinning around, she headed toward the corral and Black Jack at a dead run.

TRENT PULLED UP in the first good clump of trees he came to and settled down to watch his back trail. Where he went and how fast he traveled depended on whether or not she tried to follow him.

Sure enough, it was only a matter of a half hour or so before he saw distant movement that announced Suzannah's approach.

Swearing, he turned the mustang and set spurs to the animal's sides. If she wouldn't listen to reason, he'd simply run away from her.

Which would have worked out just fine if he hadn't suddenly realized that if he did that, he'd spend all his time worrying about her safety. He'd have to convince her she really didn't want to do this. Turning his horse, he rode back to meet her.

The joyous expression on her face when she saw him was easy enough to wipe off. All he had to do was tell her she was a pain in the neck, more trouble than she was worth, a hindrance rather than a help, and he was damned sick and tired of baby-sitting her on these nature excursions.

She listened without comment until he ran out of invective. Then she gave him a tremulous smile and said, "Yes, it's all true. I apologize. I also apologize for what happened when I went to the Crazy Ace—"

With an oath, Trent yanked his horse's head around and took off at a gallop.

She was right behind him. "It was all a terrible misunderstanding," she called. "I never meant to—I always intended to— *Trent, wait!*"

He didn't. The last thing he wanted was an apology for what had nearly happened between them in the clean fragrant straw of his barn—what he'd damned well wanted to happen.

Only she refused to give up. All day, she just kept coming on. And instead of a calm and reasoned approach to the wild-horse problem, Trent found himself in a lather about where she was at any given moment, and what she was doing, and if she was about to get herself lost, and whether she was in danger....

This had to stop. Tethering his horse out of sight, he hoisted himself onto a tree limb and waited.

Hell, if he'd been a big cat, she'd be a dead duck right now, he thought as she galloped straight up to the tree and passed beneath it. Or at least her horse did.

Suzannah herself wound up flat on her back on the ground with 190 pounds of snarling cowboy pinning her down. She looked up at him with a woozy smile.

"Go back!" he yelled at her, feeling every curve and indentation of the body beneath his.

"Never!"

She had so little breath for talking that the single word was more mouthed than said, but he got it just the same. She wasn't going to give up—but he was.

Because if he kept on this way, he was going to forget all about what he had to do and remember only what he wanted to do—to her.

He climbed off her stiffly and hobbled to his horse. "All right then, come," he flung back at her. "But don't think this changes anything."

THEY PAUSED at Little Wild Horse Creek to water their horses. They'd ridden for hours in silence, and Suzannah knew he was still angry with her, but she was willing to accept that as the price for coming along.

Trent's mustang lifted his head and snorted, ears pricking. Head high, he stared toward the foothills.

"Does he know something we don't?" she asked hopefully.

Trent nodded. "The wild herd's been here, but not recently. Looks to me like they're drifting back toward the Tall Timber Unit of the Monarch."

"Oh, no! They'll be walking right into a trap if they go onto Monarch land."

"Not necessarily." Trent lifted his reins and his horse stepped out obediently. Suzannah and Black Jack followed. "There's some pretty wild country back there, lots of brush and timber. It'd be hard to spot anything from the air, which is a definite plus."

She felt a leap of hope. She'd been conscious all day of the occasional buzz of her father's small plane overhead, and once they'd passed close to a search party, which fortunately hadn't seen them. "What cattle we've got there are pretty well contained in a few meadows," she offered.

Trent's nod signified satisfaction. "Unless you know the territory, it's not easy to get in even on horseback. The ground search should be considerably slowed, if not stopped cold."

"But won't that create just as big a problem for us?" she suggested for the sake of argument.

He flashed her the first grin she'd had from him that day. "I *know* the territory," he said.

THEY ATE A LATE LUNCH in the saddle, all the while keeping a wary eye on thunderheads boiling up in the west. Long before the first bolt of lightning split the sky, Suzannah knew they were in for it. Long steady rains were unusual in summertime, but quick and violent thunderstorms were common.

By tacit agreement, they pushed their mounts to a faster pace. In strange territory, Suzannah had no idea where they were heading, but her faith and trust in her companion were total. Lightning flashed and she glanced anxiously toward Trent for reassurance.

"There's a bluff ahead with an overhang—almost a cave," he shouted over the rumble of thunder. "We can hole up until we see how bad this is going to be. Stay with me, Suzy!"

Stay with me, Suzy! She'd do her best, Suzannah vowed silently, digging her heels into Black Jack's ribs. The first fat drops of rain plopped down, and the big gelding jumped to follow Trent's more agile mustang down a brushy slope.

Lightning played around them and one crash of thunder followed another. Suzannah clung to her horse's back with all her strength, concentrating on the task at hand. Trent rode with fluid grace, more than a match for the wiry and surefooted mustang.

Black Jack stumbled, and Suzannah grabbed the saddle horn just in time to keep from being thrown. Once more in control, she glanced up to see an expression of concern cross Trent's face. He'd dropped back to help her, she realized with a flush of pleasure.

"I'm fine," she shouted through what was now a curtain of water. "Go on!"

He nodded and gigged his horse into the lead again. Another ten minutes of slipping and sliding downhill, and he led her beneath a rocky overhang at the side of a hill.

Exhausted and breathless, Suzannah slipped from her saddle and straight into Trent's arms. How he'd dismounted so quickly and reached her side she couldn't imagine, but the fact that he was there filled her with warm gratitude.

"I thought you were going down back there," he said in a voice like gravel. "Lord, Suzy, I don't know what I'd do if—"

He broke off and she lifted her head to look into his eyes. Thunder and lightning crashed around them, but they were safe from the elements inside this sanctuary in the middle of the Wyoming wilderness.

Wet—water still streamed from their hair and plastered their clothing to their bodies—but safe.

Or am I? Suzannah wondered. She understood the look in Trent's eyes and welcomed it, along with the descent of his mouth on hers. Clinging to him, she let herself be swept away, no longer fighting the feeling that loving this man was the most natural action in her universe.

He kissed her until she was dizzy, and then he kissed her some more. She lost all sense of time and place and circumstance, content to let him carry her along with him.

She was completely unprepared when he stumbled forward with a grunt of surprise. Only his powerful embrace kept her from falling.

She forced her eyes to open. "Wh-what is it?" she murmured, still drunk with his kisses.

"Horse," he muttered, jerking his chin to one side.

Over his shoulder, Suzannah saw the mustang.

Nervous laughter, laced with relief, bubbled in her throat. "I think he's trying to tell us something."

"Yeah." For a moment Trent stared past her, beyond the narrow confines of their sanctuary. Slowly his frown melted, to be replaced by a different expression. "I think," he drawled, "that hoss is tryin' his damnedest to tell us the storm has passed."

Glancing around, Suzannah saw that it was true. Everything—trees, shrubs, grass and hills—dripped water, but the squall itself raced eastward.

"You've got a smart horse there," she said, neglecting to add that he wasn't smart enough to consider the storm inside.

"Yep, smart," Trent agreed, "but he's no mind reader."

He released her and stepped back, rubbing his palms against wet leather chaps. "I'd thought we might spend the night here, but now I see that wouldn't be such a good idea."

Suzannah licked her lips. She saw nothing to be gained by playing dumb. "No," she agreed, "it wouldn't." She waited for him to make a better suggestion, wondering what had happened to her independence. Why was she so content to follow this man's lead in all things but one? And then the answer smacked her right between the eyes: because she trusted him.

He groaned. "Don't look at me like that, Suzannah."

"Like what, Trent?"

"Like... Let's get out of here before you find out the hard way."

Grabbing her by the waist, he swung her up into Black Jack's saddle. Settling gingerly in the wet leather, she watched him mount his own horse. His expression made her shiver, despite the restored warmth of the afternoon.

Once they got out into the sunlight and started drying out, they'd all be steaming, riders and animals alike.

From the looks of him, Trent already was.

THEY RODE into the cow camp at the Tall Timber Unit right at sundown. The two cowboys assigned there stood outside their accommodations—really little more than a log shack—scratching their heads in surprise.

Suzannah swung stiffly out of the saddle. "Good evening, Mason. Got a cup of coffee you can spare?"

The smaller of the two men grinned. "For you, Suzannah? You bet!" He gestured toward the youngster at his side. "You remember my boy, Charlie? Your pa put him to work out here this summer to get all notions of cowboyin' outta his head."

Charlie dipped his chin in an embarrassed nod. A tall lanky kid of eighteen or nineteen, he towered over his wiry father.

"Sure. Good to see you again, Charlie." She indicated Trent. "Do you both know...?"

Charlie and Mason nodded enthusiastically, and the older man stepped forward with outstretched hand.

"If it ain't Jim Trent, the handiest old boy with a rope I believe I ever saw. What in the world...?"

Trent pumped the proffered hand. "Surprised you remember, Mase. I was just a pup last time we met."

"I don't forget the good'uns." Mason introduced his son, who shook hands just as eagerly, his face a study in hero worship.

"Seen you win big in Cheyenne a few years back," Charlie added. "You're really somethin'."

Trent turned aside the praise. "Afraid those glory days are behind me," he said gruffly. "At the moment, Suzy and I are hot on the trail of a band of wild horses...."

"COME AND GET IT 'fore I throw it to the dawgs!"

Mason's wake-up call dragged Suzannah from a sound sleep. Snuggling back down in her sleeping bag, she yawned and tried to force her eyes open.

They'd wanted her to take the cabin while the three men slept outside on the ground, but she wasn't having any of that. She'd come prepared to sleep beneath the stars and had refused to be forestalled.

Once convinced she meant what she said, Trent had assembled his own bedroll nearby and Charlie did likewise, not about to miss a chance for further interaction with his hero.

"You young folks are pure loco," Mason had grumbled before taking himself off to bed inside the cabin. "Have it your own way, but remember, 4:00 a.m. comes mighty danged early, especially when you been tryin' to sleep rough."

Greeted by a chorus of groans, he'd relented. "Five, then," he conceded, "in honor of the little lady. Her daddy won't mind if we lay abed an extra hour."

That, Suzannah knew, was the truth. The Monarch dispatched a two-man crew to this small isolated cabin each May to nursemaid cows on summer pasture. Without a telephone or any other means of outside communication, the cowboys were strictly on their own—and they liked it that way. This was Mason's seventh or eighth summer in the high country, and now his son had joined him.

Under normal circumstances, the two-man team was fed, saddled and gone before first light, seven days a week. They'd return twelve or more hours later to a cabin with no electricity or running water; there they'd eat and fall into bunks to get the rest they needed to do the whole thing again the next day.

"Pa says I'm crazy to want to cowboy, but I got it in my blood," Suzannah heard Charlie explain to Trent in a plaintive voice just before she fell asleep.

She could understand that. Jim Trent was in *her* blood, she was very much afraid.

SUZANNAH WAS still yawning an hour later when she crawled into the saddle and turned her horse north, following Trent deeper into the wilderness.

"We seen wild horse sign up there around Jigsaw Ridge," Mason had confided. "It's someplace to start, anyhow."

"Much obliged." Trent nodded and clucked softly to his horse.

"Good luck," Charlie called after them. "I'd sure like to be there to see what happens when you meet up with that wild stud."

Suzannah shivered. *She'd* probably be there, but she wasn't at all sure what would happen—or even what Trent wanted to happen, now.

They found Jigsaw Ridge and trouble at the same time.

CHAPTER NINE

TRENT GRABBED Black Jack's bridle to keep Suzannah from riding over the top of the rugged crest in blissful ignorance. Half dozing in the saddle, she jerked upright and gave him a startled glance.

He touched his forefinger to his lips. "I heard something," he explained in a low voice.

She glanced around, disoriented. They'd passed close to a couple of other search parties already today. It was getting crowded around here, no doubt about it.

He leaned closer. "Wait over there while I check it out."

She nodded. While Trent rode ahead, she moved off the faint trail into the trees, where she dismounted. Tying Black Jack's reins to a limb, she settled down with her back against a tree trunk.

Every slight sound made her start uneasily, yet it never occurred to her to disobey his orders. If he told her to wait, she would wait. Forty-five minutes later, her patience was rewarded.

Trent slipped back so soundlessly that he startled her all over again. "It's Rod and Uncle Henry with Martin Young—that bunch," he reported. "They didn't see me, and it looks like they're headed southwest, which'll keep them out of our way. Mount up and let's get out of here."

They'd been riding for almost two hours without seeing another soul when Trent's mustang suddenly flung up his head. With a snort of alarm, the animal danced back a few steps. So uncharacteristic was this behavior from so placid and dependable a mount that something extraordinary had to be afoot.

Turning quickly in her saddle, she saw what had alarmed the mustang: Pegasus, not an illusion, but a silver statue silhouetted on the highest ridge to the northeast.

"Trent!" She clutched his arm in her excitement.

But he was already staring at the stallion through narrowed determined eyes. At her touch, he turned with a smile so brilliant that she was lost all over again. Where he led, she would gladly follow.

SUZANNAH HAD DONE some rough riding in her time, but nothing that even approached their chase after the wild band. Following Trent, she charged hell for leather around the base of the hill where they'd seen the stallion. Sure enough, they hit the narrow trail at the bottom just a stride ahead of the wild band.

For a moment, all was chaos, the air filled with flailing hooves and the outraged squeal of the herd's monarch. Pegasus carried the day by sheer willpower, for the domesticated horses quailed before him. In a flash, he was past, shoving his mares forward with savage nips and noisy outrage.

"Wait!" Trent threw up an arm to halt Suzannah's headlong and heedless pursuit. "There's a maze of canyons up ahead. I don't know of any true box canyons, but a passel of 'em back up on rough country. If we're lucky, I'll pick one with a back trail blocked by brush and rock slides. If I'm not—'' he shrugged ''—we could lose 'em.''

Suzannah's gelding danced in a circle and she fought to calm the excited animal. "Tell me what to do!"

"Push the herd on down this trail as hard as you can. I'll take a shortcut and pick a likely opening. And Suzy—'' he held his mount back a moment longer ''—be careful. I don't want anything happening to you.''

Suzannah stood in her stirrups and leaned forward, excitement making her voice shake. "Don't worry about me! Go, Trent!"

Their gazes locked for a heart-stopping second. Then he spun his mustang and guided the animal unhesitatingly over the edge of the trail and into the abyss.

For a moment Suzannah watched his downhill slide, her heart in her mouth. Then she kicked her own horse into a gallop, following the trail of the wild herd. Black Jack stretched out, and soon they were hot on the heels of the fleeing horses.

She was as surprised as they were when Trent popped up out of nowhere to block their path. The white stallion reared, pawing the air and roaring a challenge to this new danger.

But where the stallion might have stood his ground and fought, his harem had no such intentions. Wild with fear and pressured by the oncoming rider, they took the path of least resistance. Veering left, they plunged into a narrow-necked canyon. Without slackening their pace, they ran at breakneck speed past the small waterfall tumbling over the lip of the canyon into a creek below.

Only Pegasus hesitated, swinging in a threatening circle with bowed neck and blazing eyes. Then he whirled and pounded after his mares, all soon lost in a cloud of dust.

Trent didn't follow. In a flash he was off his horse's back and dashing for one side of the canyon's narrow mouth. No more than ten feet wide, the entrance was littered with brush and debris. Working furiously, he began to erect a temporary barrier out of fallen logs and brush and even rocks, rolled laboriously into place.

Once she understood what he was trying to do, Suzannah rushed to help. Unfurling her lariat, she tossed the loop to Trent and used Black Jack to drag the heavier objects into place.

It was hot exhausting work, but that didn't faze them. The last tree branch settled into place just in the nick of time, for simultaneous with its placement, the stallion came barreling around the bend in the canyon.

Suzannah gave a little cry of panic and fell back a few steps, certain Pegasus was going to launch himself into the air and fly over this flimsy hastily-constructed barricade. But at the last moment, he turned aside and thundered back the way he'd come.

She pivoted toward Trent, her heart banging against her ribs so hard her entire body quivered. She'd never been more excited, never felt more alive, in her entire life.

"We did it!" she cried, throwing herself into his arms. "We did it! We've captured the White Stallion of the Plains! Pop and his cronies are out of luck! Oh, Trent, I can't believe it!"

Holding her by the waist, he swung her around and lifted her into the air. His excitement equaled her own, she realized in some still-coherent part of her mind. Slowly he lowered her, holding her close so that her body slid down the length of his. Her feet touched the ground, but she didn't move away.

There in the entrance to Jigsaw Canyon, just inside the makeshift fence containing the wild herd, in the midst of the dust and debris of combat and beneath a burning sun in a blazing blue sky, he took her into his arms and kissed her.

HE KNEW he was making a mistake, but dammit, she was too hard to resist. Feeling her lips soften beneath his, Trent pressed her tighter against his chest and deepened the kiss.

But even as he lost himself in her, he couldn't forget her visit to the Crazy Ace, couldn't get past the knowledge that she'd do anything—*anything*—to get her way where that herd of wild horses was concerned.

Even sleep with him? He wanted her—damn, he wanted her—but not like that, never like that. He forced himself to break off the kiss and glare down at her.

Her eyes were closed, long feathery lashes making dark smudges on her high cheekbones. Her lips, so hauntingly tender and sweet, trembled.

"Trent?" She lifted her face blindly toward his as if seeking his kiss.

If he kissed her again, it'd be all over but the shouting, he realized, for she'd win. If he kissed her again, there'd be nothing he could refuse her.

And if he kissed her again, he wouldn't stop there. He'd make love to her as he'd longed to do ever since the day so long ago he'd seen her chin-deep in Wild Horse Creek.

With a muttered oath, he scooped her up in his arms. That brought her eyes flying open. With a little gasp, she wrapped her arms around his neck. He saw the question in her eyes and knew she thought he'd carry her to some grassy glade and have his way with her.

He'd have his way with her, all right. Steeling himself against the nibbling little kisses she pressed against his throat, he strode across the uneven ground with determined steps, ignoring the twinges in his right knee.

She sighed and the hair on the nape of his neck prickled. He walked faster—no time to lose, nothing to be said. Now was time for action—

"Trent."

She whispered his name, fluttering her fingers over his ear to curve into his hair. Suffering from oxygen deprivation, he almost stumbled the last few steps.

"Trent?"

He saw her uncertainty when she opened her eyes to look up at him. Big, soft, sherry-brown eyes that couldn't be trusted.

"Suzannah," he croaked.

"Y-yes?"

"Hold your breath."

And he flung her slender body into space.

SUZANNAH HIT the surface of Jigsaw Creek and sank like a stone. She came up sputtering and furious. Struggling to her feet, she discovered the water was only waist-deep—but the splash created by the small waterfall caught her square in the face and sent her into another spasm of coughing.

Choking and fighting for air, she turned toward the bank. Trent stood there, legs spread wide and fists on his hips.

Staggering a few steps against the drag of the water, she shoved wet strands of hair out of her eyes. "Why'd you do that?" she shrieked at him. "You...you barbarian!"

"Sticks and stones," he sneered. "The 'why' should be obvious."

"It's not obvious to me!" Regaining her balance and her wits at approximately the same time, Suzannah waded out. Her long-sleeved cotton shirt clung to her, and water cascaded off her jeans. After a struggle, she dragged herself onto dry land, her boots sloshing with each step. She stood before him, miserable and confused.

His lip curled. "You never give up, do you. How far were you prepared to go the other day at the ranch?"

"You misunderstood all that. I didn't set out to—"

"Spare me." He shook his head. "If we'd gone much further, I'd have been hard-pressed to deny you anything."

She let out a sigh compounded of equal parts assent and denial. "I did go there to ask for your help," she admitted with spirit. "But I was horribly embarrassed about doing it, and then you wouldn't let me get a word in edgewise until it was too late."

"It's *my* fault now, is it?" He crossed his arms over his chest and tried to stare her down.

She refused to be cowed. "Hush and let me say this. You were so nice, and so welcoming, and I did want to see the ranch, and I did enjoy your company, and then . . .''

She stopped just short of pleading for his understanding. He wasn't going to help her, not then and certainly not now. That much was obvious in the hard slant of his jaw and the firm set of his lips. Nevertheless, she pressed on. "And then you kissed me."

"I did more than kiss you."

"Oh, yes," she agreed wholeheartedly, "and then I wasn't thinking about horses anymore. You're right, if Rod hadn't come—"

"But he did."

"Yes, he did. And you believed the worst. Why couldn't you believe the best?" She shivered beneath her clammy shirt, rubbing her arms to get her blood flowing again.

But she didn't flinch away from the censure in his eyes or try to soften her own blunders. "I went to the Crazy Ace to ask for your help, not to seduce you into doing something you didn't want to do."

"Yeah, sure."

He didn't believe her, which was no great surprise. She gave up. "Okay, so you tossed me in the creek. I'd say that just about makes us even."

"Maybe so." He jerked his chin toward the canyon. "The Monarch mares are in there, and they're none the worse for wear. I could catch 'em up and have you headed back to Addison with them in an hour."

She lifted her chin. "I'm staying."

"Aw, Suzy." His shoulders slumped and suddenly he turned pleading blue eyes on her. "I can't believe you haven't given up on those wild horses."

"Why should I? We're already way out in the middle of nowhere—we can't be that far from their home range. If we could get them started in that direction, they'd find their way."

He shook his head but without the absolute certainty she'd grown to expect. "No dice. This has become an issue with me, too. I'm damned well going to ride that stallion—at least once. Maybe then..." He shrugged and when he continued, his words came reluctantly. "Maybe then I'll let him go, if he's as untamable as you think."

"Do you mean it?" It wasn't much, but it was the closest he'd come to a concession. She took a joyous step toward him. "If you do, I'll help you any way I—"

The buzz of an airplane interrupted her. Silently she and Trent lifted their faces toward the sky, where Rex Glenn's Cessna was making a pass over the canyon. When the plane veered north, they watched it till it was out of sight.

Suzannah turned to Trent anxiously. "Do you think he saw us?"

He shook his head. "Too much greenery down here. The horses in the canyon may be a different story, though." He shrugged. "All we can do is hope they were under cover."

Saying a silent prayer, she nodded. "Then I'm going to assume we're safe."

Trent met her gaze before looking down pointedly at her wet body. Embarrassed, she drew back, automatically crossing her arms over her chest.

For a long moment he stared at her. Then he sighed. "We've got work to do," he said, his voice sharp with strain. "Let's get to it."

A TENSE TWOSOME rode into the canyon an hour later; a hot dusty twosome eventually rode out, alternately dragging and being dragged by a still-fighting white stallion. By the time they got him snubbed to a cottonwood just inside the entrance, Trent was swearing and Suzannah was beginning to wonder what she'd gotten herself into.

She'd been dead right about one thing: Pegasus was no fairy steed but a flesh-and-blood animal. Rearing, plunging, the infuriated white horse threw himself about on the end of Trent's lariat with complete disregard.

Trent grabbed his Stetson from his head and swiped at his sweaty temple with his forearm. "Damn! I think we got us a tiger by the tail."

Leaning down, he rubbed absently at his right knee. He'd be stiff and sore tomorrow, she was sure. He and his mount had taken a spectacular fall during the mad pursuit over rough terrain.

Nor had she escaped unscathed. Her hands throbbed from rope burns, and Black Jack had a welt across his flanks where a tree limb had snapped back on him.

Trent dismounted. His face glowed with perspiration but with elation, too. "Soon's I catch my breath, I'll go back in and cut out the Monarch mares," he said.

"I'll help," Suzannah offered, although she was so tired she wasn't sure she could.

He shook his head. "No need—if you promise you won't get close to that stud while I'm gone." He glanced toward the stallion, still plunging and snorting on a short tether. "I'd hate for you to take a notion to turn him loose. You could get yourself stomped to smithereens, and I sure as hell wouldn't want to try to explain that to Rex.''

Suzannah grimaced. ''I suppose that would be your only regret.''

The slow sexy smile she'd come to love curved his lips. ''No,'' he said. ''Not my *only* regret.''

THE SUN WAS DESCENDING behind the mountains to the west, and a kind of peace had settled across the land by the time Trent returned. He led two very skittish mares bearing the Monarch brand.

Even Pegasus had calmed down enough to stand at last with heaving sides and high-flung head. When Trent led the mares past, the stallion's nostrils flared and he snorted. Trent and Suzannah had captured his body, but his indomitable spirit remained untouched.

Suzannah couldn't take her gaze off the stallion. ''I wish they could see him like this,'' she said to Trent.

''They? Who?'' He sank onto a rock with a groan, stretching his legs out before him.

''The idiots who say wild horses are nothing but broomtails and jugheads, not good for anything except dog food. They should see Pegasus. He's a...a prince among horses.'' She laughed at her own fancy.

''He's a nice piece of horseflesh,'' Trent agreed, ''but he's no cream puff.''

That, unfortunately, was the truth. Pegasus carried the scars of a hundred battles on his white hide. Even so, she considered him the most beautiful sight on earth....

With the possible exception of Jim Trent, washing up later beneath the waterfall. He'd taken off his shirt and boots and chaps, and waded in wearing his jeans.

The rushing water caught and reflected the sun's rays, turning the man into a gleaming bronze statue.

She wished she could join him, but she'd already had her bath—not that she'd dare, anyway. He'd just think she was making another play for him, for her own nefarious purposes.

Why did that bother him so much? Most men in her somewhat limited experience were willing to take anything they could get anytime they could get it. Could it possibly be because he cared more for her than he was willing to let on?

As she cared for him. Fighting him had become practically second nature, but if he ever took her into his arms, looked deep into her eyes and commanded, "Trust me, Suzy," she would.

She already did.

Trent leaned over to splash water into his face, his sleek brown back rippling with muscle. She watched dreamily, rationalizing like crazy. He'd be doing the stallion a favor by breaking him. Pegasus was no spring chicken. If Trent or someone like him didn't intervene, a younger stallion was sure to come along sooner or later and take away the silver stallion's band of mares. That would leave Pegasus humiliated and alone at best, dead or injured at worst.

Or he really could end up in a can of dog food. As Rex pointed out ad infinitum, such things happened all the time. Would it be so terrible if the stallion spent the rest of his life in horse-style luxury on the Crazy Ace? There he would be safe, from her father and other predators, with everything he needed nearby.

Everything except freedom.

OVER A SUPPER of canned hash and coffee, they talked about the challenges they faced.

"If only we had more time." Suzannah sighed.

"If wishes were horses . . ." Trent's tone was ironic. "No point worryin' about what we don't have. Somebody's bound to stumble on us at any minute. When that happens, all bets are off."

She nodded dispiritedly. "Pop won't quit until that stallion's accounted for," she agreed with utter certainty. "At least now we've got him, thanks to you." She looked him full in the face, letting all her admiration and sincere appreciation shine through.

"Ah, Suzy." He banged down his tin plate. "Hell, I don't want your thanks. I want..." Firelight reflected in his eyes, lighting them as if from within.

"What?" She didn't hedge, didn't look coyly away, simply stared back at him.

He stood up slowly, as if bone-weary. His tall rangy form might have looked threatening to someone who didn't know him as she did.

"I want to settle this wild-horse standoff once and for all."

"S-so do I." She did, but that hadn't been her first desire; it was her second.

"We don't have a lot of time." He spoke urgently. "The stallion has to be broken, and fast, at least green-broke. Once that's accomplished, your father can stomp and bellow all he wants, but there won't be a damned thing he can do about it." His eyes narrowed to slits. "Are you with me on this, Suzannah?"

She might escape the rock if she settled for the hard place. She should; she wanted to.

She couldn't, not yet. "You're right, I know," she said slowly, "but I need time to think. You can't do anything until tomorrow, anyway."

For a moment he stood as still as the shadowed outline of the mountains behind him. Then he nodded. "We'll hold off until tomorrow, then. In the meantime, you'd better get some rest." He looked past her into the shadowy hills. "I'm going to take a look around, climb to the top of that bluff behind us and see if I can spot any campfires. I've got a hunch... Don't wait up for me."

Turning, he took two steps and his right knee buckled. She jumped up, ready to rush to his aid, but he caught his balance and with a curse, strode into the darkness beyond the flickering firelight.

What had happened? Puzzling over it, she listened to him moving around, checking their horses hobbled in the meadow. His footsteps faded and then there was nothing but the usual night sounds.

Only after he'd gone did she realize she should have called him back and confronted him with the question preying on her mind. Had he given up rodeo and retired to the Crazy Ace because of an injury? Just what sort of trouble was that knee giving him? Would riding Pegasus or any other bucking bronco be dangerous—more dangerous than usual for the most dangerous sport in the world?

For a few minutes, she sat staring into the fire, struggling with her dilemma. She was tired of fighting him, but she couldn't go along with his stated intention to ride the stallion if it might put him in danger.

Maybe she should turn Pegasus loose before Trent returned.

Twisting, she looked up into the hills. He could be watching her right now, waiting for her to make a wrong move. But she didn't think that was the case.

She thought, in fact, that he trusted her more now than when they'd caught the horses earlier today. She thought he'd begun to believe her explanation for going to the Crazy Ace.

Groaning, she stared at the full moon, drawing up her legs so she could rest her chin on her knees. She didn't want to betray him, but she also didn't want anything bad to happen to him.

Unfortunately somewhere along the line her motivations had gotten all mixed up. No longer was this the cut-and-dried case it'd been. Now she was more concerned for the man than she was for the horse.

Jumping up, she walked outside the circle of light and stood with her back to the fire, breathing hard. She didn't want Trent riding that wild stallion—but this time it wasn't for the animal's sake but for the man's. Although Trent might never understand what she was about to do, she was doing it for him.

And she had to hurry.

CHAPTER TEN

ONCE AWAY from the light of the fire, Suzannah's eyes adjusted quickly to the illumination cast by a full moon. Certainly she could see well enough to untie the ropes reinforcing the weakest part of the makeshift fence at the canyon's mouth and drag aside the smallest of the branches and rocks.

Pegasus watched her work, his ears pricked forward. In the shadowy light, he looked ghostlike. Her scalp prickled as if someone was watching her. But the white stallion, although smart, wasn't a someone, wasn't human, she derided herself.

To survive in the wild, a mustang had to be born both smart and tough and get smarter and tougher fast—survival of the fittest in the most grueling sense. Pegasus hadn't assumed the mantle of monarch of a band of mares and managed to keep it all these years without possessing the highest qualities of his breed and then some.

Perhaps he'd even be smart enough to realize she was trying to help him, maybe even save his life. She hoped so, because there would be no second chances. Glancing toward the bluff where Trent had disappeared, she prayed he'd take his time—and that the animal tethered nearby would respond to the goodwill she bore him.

He didn't. Snubbed up tight against the tree with no room to retreat, Pegasus gave a low snort of warning and leaned back on the rope. To him, she was just another predator.

"Easy, boy, easy." She approached cautiously, her heart in her throat. She wasn't afraid of him—exactly. But neither was she confident.

The stallion lowered his head and for the first time, his gaze met hers, the whites of his eyes showing in the shadowy moonlight. "Take it easy," she murmured. "I'm doing this for your own good, you know."

Pegasus snorted and jerked hard against the restraint of the rope around his neck. But when she continued to stand there murmuring in a low hypnotic voice, he quieted again, although he continued to breathe heavily.

Suzannah's heart beat so fast and hard she had to exercise iron self-control to keep her voice calm and gentle. Bringing all her concentration to bear, she took one slow and easy step, and then another, pausing after each to let the stallion become accustomed to a new perspective. Every time she moved, he blew soft warnings through his nostrils and yanked at the tether before settling down again.

Eventually, she succumbed to the mesmerizing sound of her own voice. The world closed in around her until there was nothing left except her intense desire to communicate with the stallion. She wanted to hurry, needed to hurry, yet she forced herself to take it slow and easy, knowing that anything else would spook the horse and destroy any chance she had for success.

And then at last, she found herself standing almost eyeball to eyeball with the silver stallion. Reaching out one trembling hand, she touched his arched neck for the very first time.

Muscles bunched and trembled beneath the satiny hide, but that was all. She held her breath, slowly raising her other hand to fumble at the knotted rope. The stallion rolled his eyes and his nostrils flared with the force of his noisy breathing, but he held steady.

Breathlessly she worked at the knot, ignoring the scratch of coarse Manila hemp against her fingers— and then she had it. The knot unfurled beneath her hand.

With a harsh cry, the stallion reared, ripping the loosened rope from between her fingers. For a moment he towered above her, so near that his front legs flashed over her head.

Caught completely by surprise, she stumbled backward, bumping into the cottonwood tree from which the other end of the rope dangled. The stallion came down hard on the packed earth, his flailing hooves brushing her leg. With a howl that sent icy chills down her back, Pegasus lunged past, charging for the opening she'd made at the canyon's mouth.

Clinging limp and breathless to the tree, she listened to the sounds of flight. Her head spun with the aftereffects of her physical encounter with the stallion but also from the mental exertion of what she'd done.

Somewhere beyond the barrier, Pegasus squealed in outrage. Something was wrong. Still groggy, she realized she no longer heard the stallion's steady hoofbeats but, instead, the unmistakable sounds of a struggle. Pushing away from the tree, she ran toward the opening and through.

She spotted Pegasus at once. He was thrashing about on his side with Trent's lariat around his two front legs, fighting like a wildcat for his freedom.

Trent was at the other end of the rope, and he shot her a glance so murderous she wanted to turn and run.

Pegasus didn't give up without a struggle. Even when he was once more tied to his tree, he continued to throw himself against the rope and thrash about.

Suzannah stood with hanging head, afraid even to look at Trent. She was sure he'd really hate her now, and he had every right. She had betrayed him. He'd never believe she'd done it for his good and not for her own, or even the stallion's.

He didn't say a word until he'd repaired the hole she'd made in his wall. Then he turned on her, a darker shadow in the night. "I can't leave you alone for a minute, can I," he demanded in a raspy voice. "Dammit, Suzannah!"

She fought the tears welling in her eyes. "What can I say, Trent? That I'm sorry? I'm not! I'm just sorry you didn't get back five minutes later."

He laughed harshly. "I thought we'd agreed to hold off doing anything until tomorrow." He shook his head with sharp disgust. "I sure as hell underestimated your feelings for that damned horse."

Her stomach clenched. "No, Trent," she said recklessly, "you underestimated my feelings for you."

Turning, she headed for the low-burning campfire. She'd taken only a couple of steps before his hands on her shoulders stopped her progress and spun her around.

"Explain that," he demanded, his fingers digging.

"I put two and two together, that's all. I was afraid the stallion would hurt you."

"I can take care of myself," he said angrily. "Hell, I've ridden more buckers than you'll ever see."

"Which one of them hurt you bad enough to take you out of rodeo?"

He sucked in his breath. "Rod told you." He sounded as if that was another betrayal. "I didn't even know he knew."

"Rod didn't tell me. No one did. I've got eyes. You were limping even before you took that fall back in the canyon today. You massage your right knee almost automatically." With nothing to lose, she ignored his glowering anger. "I'd guess it happened about six months ago. Am I right?"

"What the . . . ? How'd you figure that?"

"You missed Ace's funeral."

His hands fell from her shoulders and he stared at her, his shock almost palpable. She could go now, away from him, but not away from what she was feeling. So she simply stood there, hoping he could see the truth in her face or hear it in her voice or feel it in the air he breathed.

She even found the fortitude to press her case. "I couldn't bear the thought of you being hurt," she said simply. "When I realized, well, that's when it got personal for me. My stand on the wild horses is a matter of principle, but you...your well-being is more than principle. Say you believe me, Trent."

"Yeah, I believe you."

Amazed, she demanded, "Then why are you still so mad at me? I didn't break any promises. I honestly thought I was doing what was best. I hear such anger in your voice."

"That's not anger." He held himself stiffly, his arms straight at his sides and his shoulders back. "It's fear. It's terror."

He pulled her into his arms then, dragging her against his chest and holding her there, although resistance was the farthest thing from her mind. The frantic beating of his heart pounded in her ears.

He spoke, his mouth pressed against her hair and muffling his voice. "You could have been killed. When that stallion came charging through the opening, all I could think was that he'd left you trampled in the dirt back there somewhere. You think at that moment I cared what happened to the wild horses? I had my rope in my hand—I threw it more out of instinct than anything else. If you'd been hurt or—" he tightened his embrace "—worse, I'd have turned that horse over to your father so fast—"

"Shh." She kissed his throat, feeling the icy fear that encased her heart melting away. "He didn't hurt me, and I hope he didn't hurt you, either—and we didn't hurt him. I remember once hearing you say that all's well that ends well. This is ending just fine...."

"This isn't ending at all."

Tilting her face, he kissed her gently, then with passion. Releasing her mouth, he picked her up in his arms and carried her into their camp.

He stopped, his feet at the edge of her bedroll, and looked down at her with a question in his eyes. She responded by lifting herself enough to touch her lips to his.

His ragged sigh spoke volumes. "Are you sure?" he demanded, his voice a harsh whisper. "Because if you're not..."

"I'm sure," she murmured, caressing his cheek with her hand. "That's an easy question because..."

He knelt, placing her gently on the sleeping bag. "Easy?" His taut laugh lacked humor.

She cupped his firm jaw with her hands and smiled. "It's easy...because I've fallen in love with you. Or maybe I've loved you since that day you found me swimming in Wild Horse Creek. The truth of the matter is I love you, Jim Trent. I adore you and..."

The rest was lost in the passion of his kiss. But when they made love, she knew it really *was* love.

AWAKENING SLOWLY the next morning, Suzannah yawned and stretched luxuriously before opening her eyes. She knew instantly that Trent was not beside her but knew with equal certainty that he was nearby, for she felt safe and happy and...

In love. She stifled what could only have been a silly giggle. It had taken her a long time, but at last she'd found the man she wanted to spend the rest of her life with.

That private acknowledgment astounded her so much her eyes popped open. The first thing she saw was Trent. Overwhelmed by the power of her feelings, she gave him a melting smile.

He didn't smile back. "Coffee's almost ready," he said, looking everywhere but at her. "Want some?"

"Y-yes." Deflated and confused, she slipped into her jeans and shirt. Something was terribly wrong.

She walked to one of the logs marking the perimeter of their camp circle and sat down, feeling awkward and ill at ease. He handed her a tin cup of coffee. She stared at it as if she'd never seen such a thing, in the process also staring at his boots.

Those boots shifted uneasily. "Uh...I've got some thinking to do, Suzannah. I also need to scout around in those hills a bit more. I was just waiting for you to wake up before I..."

She looked up into his face, realizing she'd never heard him sound uncertain before. She'd scared him last night when she mentioned love, she supposed.

Well, tough! She'd scared herself, too. It wasn't easy to tell a man who'd never betrayed more than a lustful interest in you that you loved him. It gave him a terrible power to hurt. So why was *he* standing there hemming and hawing?

"Okay, I'm awake," she said shortly, looking toward the hills. Damn, another beautiful golden day. "I'll be here when you get back, but so will all your problems."

"Problems?"

"I mean," she said sweetly, "the wild horses—they'll be here, too. Have a nice ride."

She sat there long after he'd gone, her coffee cooling but untasted. *Now I've gone and done it,* she berated herself. After waiting so long for Mr. Right, she'd fallen in love with a man who apparently didn't have a clue what love was all about.

What she should do, she decided, was spare herself further humiliation by leaving before he returned. She had a general idea of where she was and could certainly find her way back home eventually. She had plenty of food, a good horse, lots of time.

Too bad she'd as good as promised she wouldn't release the wild herd. Sometimes her own stupidity amazed her; he hadn't asked for her promise; she'd volunteered it. Maybe that meant it didn't count.

Of course it counted. She wouldn't go behind his back, not after all they'd been through together. Nor would she ever *turn* her back. She'd love Jim Trent until the day she died, even if he never reciprocated her feelings.

So instead of running away as she longed to do, she set about putting their camp to rights, caring for Black Jack, planning lunch. She was opening a can of spaghetti when she heard the thunder of a running horse.

Let it be Trent, she prayed. *Please let it be Trent!*

It was. He came barreling down the hill at a pace so reckless it made her stomach clench in panic. His mustang slid and stumbled and roared into camp as if pursued by the devil.

Leaping from the saddle, Trent met her halfway. "They're coming," he said tersely, grabbing her by the elbows.

"Who's coming?"

"Your father and half of Addison County." He glanced over his shoulder as if he expected to see a war party riding over the crest of the hill. "They spotted me across a valley, but they'll find and follow my trail without too much trouble. They'll be here soon, so we'd better get busy."

"Busy doing what?"

"I'll tell you while I throw a saddle on Black Jack," he said. "Move it, honey. We haven't lost yet!"

REX AND A DOZEN RIDERS thundered down to the canyon entrance a few hours later. Suzannah and Trent were waiting.

He turned to her with a smile. "Here goes nothing," he said almost lightly. Then his expression changed, became deeply serious. "Still love me, Su-zannah?"

She caught her breath on a gasp. Since he'd ridden in to sound the alarm, not a personal word had passed between them. They'd done what they'd had to do with a minimum of conversation; there hadn't been time to speak of personal things.

Until now. Did she love him? "Lord, yes," she choked, her heart threatening to burst with emotion. "I love you."

His broad smile outshone the sun. "Then we have nothing to worry about." He gave her a cocky grin and slid one arm around her waist before leading her forward to meet the posse.

Rex, red-faced and sweaty in the lead, hulled his rawboned gelding to a halt so he could glower down at the pair on the ground. A mare whinnied. "Hot damn!" the big man exclaimed, glancing past them toward the still-blockaded entrance. "We got that outlaw hoss this time!"

"Now, Rex—" Trent's measured tone was border-line insolent "—climb down and let's talk about this. Reasonable men can reach reasonable compro-mises."

An appeal to reason didn't appear to mean much to Rex. "Don't sweet-talk me, Trent," he bellowed. "Once I settle with that wild herd, I'll be back to set-tle up with *you*. Luring my little girl out here all alone, playing fast and loose..."

Suzannah groaned, feeling her cheeks grow hot with embarrassment. "Nobody lured me!" she snapped at her father. "I followed him—forced him to bring me with him. I'm an adult. I'm twenty-six years old and I won't have you treating me like—"

"Easy, sweetheart." Trent grinned at her before turning his impudent glance on her father. "Rex Glenn, I love your daughter and I'm going to marry her, if she'll have me. Now why don't you and the posse just take your two mares and go home?"

Suzannah turned to Trent, her lips parted in dawning wonder. "You *love* me? You want to *marry* me?"

His eyes gleamed. "Mind if we talk about that after this raiding party moves on?"

She shook herself free of the mesmerizing spell of blue eyes. "Oh, sure, of course."

Rex continued to look down on them from the saddle, his expression, for once, unreadable to the daughter who knew him better than anyone in the world. Apparently Trent's announcement had stopped her father in his tracks.

"Take your mares, Pop," she urged, pressing closer to Trent's side. "That's what you came for, isn't it?"

"That, and a whole lot more." Rex's horse, sensing his rider's agitation, couldn't seem to stand still. Rex fought the fidgeting animal, swearing under his breath.

Mount finally under control, he spoke to his men. "Take down that barricade," he directed curtly, jerking his chin to indicate the brush-and-stone fence blocking the canyon's narrow entrance.

"Hold on there." Trent's voice commanded attention. "What if I gave my personal guarantee that the white stallion won't cause you any more trouble. Would that stop you?"

Rex crossed his hands over the saddle horn, reins dangling loosely between his fingers. "No, son," he said, "it wouldn't. You see, I got me a personal score to settle with that mustang. So unless you're prepared to do more than talk—" he glanced significantly at his daughter, then back at Trent "—I suggest you stand aside."

For a charged moment, it looked as if Trent might indeed be prepared to do more than talk. Then he stepped aside and waved the horse vigilantes forward with a disgusted gesture. A half dozen or more riders leapt to the ground, and within minutes the barricade it had taken so long to construct was swept aside.

Rex lifted his hand in a signal to his men, then let it fall. The riders swept past Trent and Suzannah without a glance, all except Rod. Sawing on the reins to hold back his lathered mount, he looked over at them, a slight smile playing around his lips.

"Damn!" he said. "Damn, this is good news. I got some good news of my own, Trent. She said yes!" Without waiting for a response, he gigged his horse after the rest of the riders, and they thundered out of sight around the bend.

For a moment Trent and Suzannah stared at each other, and then both burst out laughing.

"What was that supposed to mean?" she asked, her gaze following Rod as he galloped off.

Trent kissed her temple. "Jenny. Sounds like he finally got around to asking."

"Oh, Trent!" Suzannah hugged him. "I'm so happy for them." Blinking away sentimental tears, she turned toward camp. "The men will be wanting coffee when they get back."

"In a minute, honey. First I've got a few things to say."

She looked at him, mute with fear of something she couldn't name.

"I really did go out there this morning to think," he said a little defensively. "And not just about my knee—you're right about that, by the way. Rodeo's out, so if any of that's important to you, now's the time—"

Her quick incredulous laughter brought a sheepish grin from him.

"Okay, but I had to know. Because it would matter to most of the women I've met since I went on the circuit... Well, we don't want to talk about that."

"*Yet,*" she conceded with an impish smile.

He groaned good-naturedly and together they strolled toward camp.

She wrapped an arm around his waist, delighting in his across her shoulders. "Why were you so insistent about riding the stallion if you'd been hurt seriously enough to give up rodeo?"

For a moment he was silent. Then he asked rhetorically, "Why do men climb mountains? Your Pegasus—"

"He was *never* my Pegasus."

"Sorry. The white stallion was going to be my last hurrah. I didn't give up rodeo, honey. It gave up on me. I guess I did have something to prove—that I could still cut it, at least one more time. What better way to go out than astride a legend? And if the horse won, what the hell difference would it have made?"

"Jim Trent!" Appalled, she stepped in front of him and pounded a clenched fist lightly on his chest. "How can you say a stupid thing like that?"

"Because," he said gently, "it's true—*was* true. That's all changed now. I've got way too much to live for to keep on taking stupid chances. Suzannah—" he drew her into his arms and she went willingly, laying her cheek on his chest "—I meant what I said to your father, and I didn't say it just to rattle his cage. I love you. *I love you*. Will you marry me?"

"Will the sun rise in the east tomorrow?" She clung to him with all her might. "Will my father come riding out of that canyon in a couple of hours madder than a bear with a sore paw? *Yes*, Jim Trent, a thousand times, yes! I'll marry you."

THE MIGHTY HORSE-HUNTERS returned at dusk, grimfaced and silent. There wasn't a sign of a wild horse to be seen, much less a white stallion.

After the horses were unsaddled and cared for, the men clomped into camp, a disgruntled group if Suzannah had ever seen one. She poured coffee until the pot was empty, then set about making more.

Only then did she turn to her father, plant her hands on her hips and demand, "Well? What happened?"

Rex let out a blue streak of profanity that made Suzannah gasp.

"Good grief, Pop, what on earth . . . ?"

Rex threw his tin coffee cup onto the ground and stomped on it. Then he took a deep breath and sat down on a log.

"Gone." His disbelief echoed strongly in his incredulous tone. "Gone, every single last dad-burned one of them wild horses, gone without a trace. We scoured that canyon high and we scoured it low. There's hoss sign all over the place but not one animal did we find."

Rod, who had been reclining by the fire propped on his saddle, sat up. "Impossible but true. We know the herd was in there, and if they'd come out we'd have seen another set of tracks. Yet they're gone. It's the damnedest thing."

"I'm beginnin' to wonder if we know a horse from a goat," Martin Young grumbled. "Because that band was back there sure as the dickens, and now it ain't."

Henry Lowell looked slowly around the circle. "Maybe Suzannah and them kids she keeps throwin' in our faces have been right all along," he suggested into the sudden silence.

"About what?" Rex blustered.

"Maybe that danged horse really *is* Pegasus, 'cause the only way he could get out of there was if he flew— and took his whole damned harem with him."

In the flickering light of the fire, the men exchanged uneasy glances. Even Suzannah felt an eerie little prickle slide down her spine.

"Way I look at it," Rex declared, breaking the uncomfortable silence, "is that Trent and Suzannah have got a whole lot of explaining to do." He turned the full force of his glare on the two of them, sitting side by side on a log.

"Like hell," Trent said pleasantly. "I've already told you all you need to know—well, nearly all. Your daughter said yes, Rex. She'll marry me and move out to the Crazy Ace where we'll raise horses and kids in just about equal numbers."

Suzannah slid closer to throw her arms around the man she loved. "That's right, Pop." Over Trent's shoulder, she watched her father. "The one man in the county you didn't try to foist off on me, and look what happens!"

"Well, if that don't beat all! You mean I've got to spend the next twenty-five years arguing with the both of you now?" Rex threw his hat on the ground but apparently found it impossible to keep up the charade any longer. A huge smile split his face.

The last thing Suzannah saw before Trent kissed her was her father's satisfied wink.

EPILOGUE

"THEY'RE HERE, honey."

At her husband's announcement, Suzannah looked up from the smiling infant in her arms. As always, her heart gave a little leap of joy at the sight of the man who'd brought her so much happiness as a wife and mother at her new home on the Crazy Ace Ranch.

Trent lounged in the doorway, grinning at his family. He'd taken to married life with as much enthusiasm as she had, and to fatherhood, too. Now he crossed the living room to her side. She sat on a wooden rocking chair constructed long ago by Ace Kilmer himself. Trent smiled down at his son.

Little Jimmy Trent, two months old, gurgled and flailed about with tiny fists, his dark blue eyes squinting at his daddy.

"Let me take 'im," Trent urged, looking as if his fingers itched to get hold of the sturdy infant. "You can go on out and greet the thundering herd."

"All right." Suzannah stood, depositing the beloved bundle in his daddy's arms. Rising on tiptoe, she planted a kiss on Trent's lean cheek. "I love you," she whispered.

He gave her a quick grin and an equally quick arching of his brows. "I love you, too." He addressed the child in his arms. "Mama does good work, eh, partner?"

Laughing, Suzannah almost skipped through the door into the Wyoming sunshine. She was just in time to see Jenny, six months pregnant and showing it, throw open the door of the minivan for the load of children to come tumbling out.

"Ohh, Miss Glenn—I mean, Mrs. Trent!"

Suzannah's personal Greek chorus clustered around: Jessica, Ashley, Brittany, and young Master Joshua, the naysayer.

"Where's the baby?" the girls shrieked, jumping up and down in excitement.

"Where's the colt?" Joshua tried to overwhelm them with sheer lung power.

Trent strolled out the front door, little Jimmy in his arms, and the girls rushed to admire the baby. Jenny crossed to stand beside Suzannah.

Suzannah smiled at her best friend. "Thanks for bringing the kids out to visit," she said. "How'd the reading program go?"

"Fine, but I'll be glad to give it back to you next summer." Jenny made a face. "So how're you doing? Been getting much sleep? I understand new babies aren't very considerate in that regard."

"Enough to get by on," Suzannah said, doting on the sight of her tall handsome rancher-husband showing off his firstborn. "And once in a while, Trent actually helps."

"Will wonders never cease. When our turn comes, I hope Rod hears about that." Jenny leaned back against the van with a sigh. "So, what do you hear from the newlyweds?"

"What you'd expect—'Having a wonderful time, glad you're not here.' I can hardly blame them—they waited so long to be together."

"How true," agreed Jenny, who didn't know the half of it.

But Suzannah did. When Rex Glenn married Miss Louise Addison on a beautiful summer day six weeks ago, it had brought to happy conclusion a love story half a century old.

On that same day, Rex had presented his new grandson a gift no one else could have given: a pure white foal, product of the unsanctioned liaison between a Monarch mare and the wild white stallion.

"Who wants to see the colt?" Trent asked suddenly.

"I do! I do!" the children shouted.

Jenny stepped forward, arms outstretched. "I'd rather hold the most beautiful baby in the world, if you don't mind."

"Not at all," Trent agreed smugly, placing Jimmy in her eager embrace. "You need all the practice you can get, mama-to-be."

Trent led the four excited children toward the corrals, Jenny and Suzannah trailing behind. The baby was in fine form, cooing and bestowing his smiles without favoritism.

By the time they strolled around the barn, Trent was kneeling beside the spindly-legged white colt with one arm across the youngster's back, so the children could pet and fuss over him. The gentle mare stood nearby, wearing an expression as close to equine puzzlement as Suzannah had ever seen.

"Guess what they want to name him?" Trent said to Suzannah.

"Pegasus!" shrieked the children, so loudly they startled the would-be recipient of that proud name.

"I don't know..." Suzannah frowned, pretending uncertainty. "I thought maybe I'd name him...oh, I don't know...Silver?"

"That's the Lone Ranger's horse!" Joshua objected.

"Snowball?"

"That's my cat's name!" Jessica looked affronted.

"Oh." Suzannah pretended to consider. Aware of the anxious expressions of the children, she didn't drag it out too long. "All right, then." She threw up her hands. "Pegasus, by popular demand."

Jenny had watched with a smile on her face. "You've just made four kids very happy," she said, "so how about making *me* happy. I still don't understand what happened to that wild herd last summer, unless they really did sprout wings and fly out of that canyon."

Trent released the colt and the youngster frolicked off across the corral on long skinny legs, kicking out with the sheer joy of being alive. Trent gave Jenny an oblique glance. "You know," he said, managing somehow to keep a straight face, "that might not be such a bad guess."

Suzannah hid her own smile as memories flooded back. She and Trent had worked desperately to clear the hidden and dangerously narrow path leading over the back rim of Jigsaw Canyon. They'd driven the wild herd up and over, then closed the trail again and swept away telltale sign.

Thank heaven Trent knew the area as well as he did. Thank heaven for Trent, period.

The disappearance of an entire wild band had become another of the legends surrounding the mysterious white mustang. Only two people knew the truth—and they weren't about to tell.

"Well," Jenny said, "whatever happened, there's a rumor making the rounds that a herd of wild horses led by a white stallion's been spotted a couple of mountain ranges away. Do you suppose...?"

Suzannah and Trent looked at each other and burst out laughing.

If Pegasus, Sr., was out there somewhere, he and any of his kin were welcome on the Crazy Ace.

Wild horses? Anytime!

MILLS & BOON®

Next Month's Romances

Each month you can choose from a wide variety of romance novels from Mills & Boon. Below are the new titles to look out for next month from the Presents™ and Enchanted™ series.

Presents™

MISSION: MAKE-OVER	Penny Jordan
BRIDE REQUIRED	Alison Fraser
UP CLOSE AND PERSONAL!	Sandra Field
RELUCTANT FATHER!	Elizabeth Oldfield
THE VALENTINE AFFAIR!	Mary Lyons
A NANNY IN THE FAMILY	Catherine Spencer
TRIAL BY SEDUCTION	Kathleen O'Brien
HIS TEMPORARY MISTRESS	Emma Richmond

Enchanted™

A RUMOURED ENGAGEMENT	Catherine George
BEAUTY AND THE BOSS	Lucy Gordon
THE PERFECT DIVORCE!	Leigh Michaels
BORROWED—ONE BRIDE	Trisha David
SWEET VALENTINE	Val Daniels
KISSING CARLA	Stephanie Howard
MARRY ME	Heather Allison
A HUSBAND MADE IN TEXAS	Rosemary Carter

H1 9801

MILLS & BOON®

Especially for you on
Mother's Day

Four fabulous new heart-warming romances
inside one attractive gift pack.

JUST FOR A NIGHT - Miranda Lee

A MAN WORTH WAITING FOR - Helen Brooks

TO DR CARTWRIGHT, A DAUGHTER
- Meredith Webber

BABY SWAP - Suzanne Carey

Special Offer—1 book FREE!
Retail price only £6.60

On sale February 1998

*Available from WH Smith, John Menzies, Martins,
Tesco, Asda and all good book stockists*

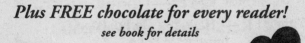

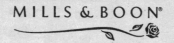

MILLS & BOON®

Back by Popular Demand

COLLECTOR'S EDITION

A collector's edition of favourite titles from one of Mills & Boon's best-loved romance authors.

Don't miss this wonderful collection of sought-after titles, now reissued in beautifully matching volumes and presented as one cherished collection.

Look out next month for:

Title #11   A Haunting Compulsion
Title #12   Images of Love

Available wherever Mills & Boon books are sold